THE QUEEN'S BUSH

A Tale of the Early Days of Bruce County

BY

W. M. BROWN, M.D.

LONDON

JOHN BALE, SONS & DANIELSSON, LTD.

83-91, GREAT TITCHFIELD STREET, W.1

—

1932

[*All Rights Reserved*]

Richardson, Bond & Wright Limited, Owen Sound, Ont., 1967

In this Record of the Queen's Bush, it may be stated that the great majority of the incidents and occurrences noted therein are true and based on fact. A little poetic license has been used in Chapter XXXII in regard to the means of frustrating Justice, but in justification it may be stated that for over 50 years it has been a Tradition in the Bruce Country that the murderer did survive the Gallows.

FOREWORD

"Books delight us when prosperity smiles; they stay to comfort us when cloudy fortune frowns. They lend strength to human compacts, and without them grave judgments may not be propounded". So wrote fourteenth century English bibliophile, writer and bishop, Richard de Bury, in his *"Philobiblon"*. And says Ecclesiastes, "of the making of many books there is no end". Of works on history, however, there can be none too many, provided it contains something new or says what has been said in a new and better way.

"The Queen's Bush — A Tale of the Early Days of Bruce County" by Dr. W.M. Brown, abounds in these ingredients. Here is a mint; it has brought together and thus makes current coin of ore otherwise widely scattered in journals, magazines and transactions.

For the newcomer to Bruce County, its pages arouse interest. For those who had been born and raised in the area and who had left it, here are components of nostalgia; for those whose birth-place it is and who live here, the past in it has its lessons for the present, for, in panorama over the years is life *par excellence* in form and manifestation — struggle but not without some leisure; sorrow but also joy; uncertainity but also assurance.

All such books suffer inexoribly the fate of *Anno Domini;* they disappear. Indeed, therefore, was the reprinting of 'The Queen's Bush', as its companion, 'Home of My Youth', by Josephine Elizabeth Hahn, a worthy Centennial Project.

"Death comes soon or late". To the heirs of Dr. W.M. Brown the Hanover Public Library is, therefore, deeply indebted for their permission to reprint this book. In turn, is the hope that the compliment implied in the wish to reprint this book particularly will be of some satisfaction to those who had permitted it.

CONTENTS.

THE QUEEN'S BUSH.

CHAPTER I.

DESCRIPTION.

IN that pleasant land, watered by the Rivers Maitland and Saugeen, in North-western Ontario, where now are smiling fields and cosy farmhouses, pleasant glades and purling spring brooks, where verdant and prolific fields lift smiling faces to an azure sky, there was in the year 1851 one vast and primeval forest, extending on the east from the line of the Holland River, Lake Simcoe and the Home District westwards, to the sounding shores of the Huron Sea.

To the southward, Fergus and Guelph were on the fringes of civilization. From that fringe, a finger-thrust of civilization—the Garafraxa Road—had been pierced northwestwards by the Government of Upper Canada, in the year 1839, to strike the shores of the Georgian Bay, at the townsite of Sydenham, at the southern end of Owen Sound Bay.

The shores of the Great Lake to the westwards offered easy access to this New Land for prospectors and pioneers from Goderich and the Huron Tract to the south. A few scattered settlers—mostly fishermen —were located at the mouth of the Saugeen River, now Southampton.

To the northward, the Georgian Bay stretched its length along the lonely shores of Grey and Bruce and bathed the rocky and silent beaches of the Indian Peninsula. Over this vast region all was pristine forest. Wild animals roamed at will. Deer and bear and wolves were plentiful and rivers and streams teemed with succulent fish.

Indians, the descendants of the ancient Objibway nation, the conquerors of the fierce Iroquois—those wild forest tigers—who had destroyed the Huron nation of this region shortly after Champlain's time, now roamed its forest aisles and followed the chase or fished its streams.

In the year 1848, the increasing human tide from across the Western Ocean, in the immigration of that and the previous year, demanded new lands for its sustenance and caused the opening up of " The Queen's Bush.'' The fisherman from the Western Isles of Scotland—from Mull and from Tiree and Coll, and from Uist and Skye, and from Islay; the cotter from the more populous parts of its southern mainland; the English-man from the provinces; the Irishman from rack-renting landlords and the potato blight of that and the previous year; the Frenchman and the German—all were rushing to that Western Eldorado, where homes and sustenance awaited them in plenty.

In that distant time things were not as now. No telephones, no wireless telegraphy nor autos were then in use. The world then was far apart. News travelled slowly. Money was counted in sterling or Halifax currency. Dollars and cents were unknown until 1858. The newcomer in that new land had to depend upon his own strong back and broad shoulders in his fight to conquer the forest and wrest a home from the Bush. He faced the latter with a stout heart and a keen axe.

The first settlers of Grey and Bruce were men of iron

vigour, who underwent labour and hardship and destitution in their battle to overcome the mantle with which Nature had covered the land, in order to hew out a home for themselves and their loved ones. He who wanders into our own Great West—on the Portage Plains : on the prairies of Saskatchewan—that bread-basket of the Dominion—on the rolling lands of sunny Alberta or in far-away Columbia, by the blue waters of Balboa's western sea, will meet the children of these pioneers of Bruce and Grey, and their hearts always fondly turn to and cherish the old home land and the old home ties back in "The Queen's Bush."

The first settlers of Upper Canada were men from many lands. The British Isles formed the chief quota :

> " Men from Severn and from Tweed
> And from the banks of Shannon!"

But French Canadians from Lower Canada settled along the upper reaches of the St. Lawrence. Further west came the Scotch settlers to Glengarry, the Perth Settlement near Ottawa. To the shores of Quinte and the Niagara Peninsula came these devoted men, who left homes and surroundings in the Republic to the south—the United Empire Loyalists. To facilitate the settlement of Upper Canada a great land company was formed, called the Canada Company, with John Galt as its President. The first town founded by them in Upper Canada was Guelph. This company also opened up the Huron Tract and founded its chief town, Goderich.

The new settler, wishing to locate in the Bush, first equipped himself for a prospecting tour. Leaving his family "down below," that is, in the older and more settled parts of the province, he provided himself with a pack in which were cooking utensils—frying pan, cup, knife and fork, spoon, flour, salt, tea, bacon and matches, an axe, auger and chisel, and a gun and blanket.

Thus equipped, he struck into the Bush, following a surveyor's "blaze" which marked the different lines of the township. After days of wanderings, sleeping sometimes at a settler's shanty, sometimes at the foot of trees, rolled in his blanket, and knowing that good

THE CAMP FIRE.

hardwood timber—beech and maple and elm—indicated good soil, and if in the neighbourhood of a good spring of clear water he would decide to take up his land.

To do so and prevent others "jumping" his claim he felled trees to make a clearing, chopped and logged the wood and brush into piles, which on drying could be burned, and erected a shanty. When hunger over-took him in the forest he built a fire, mixed some flour with water and a little salt into scones, which he baked in a frying pan over his camp fire. Or his gun might bring down a brace of pigeons—of which great numbers flew in flocks over the land—or a rabbit of partridge or wild duck from the streams.

His location decided upon, he began the building of his shanty. Trees were felled and chopped into logs. The logs were dressed on one side only, and notched to dovetail at the corners and roofed with hemlock bark or split cedar shingles, with rough openings for doorway and windows. There the pioneer lived until compelled by depleting stores of food to leave the " Bush " and once more visit "the Front," where a stay of a few months working for a farmer in the older settled parts of the province allowed the settler to renew his finances before returning to the " Bush."

If single, on his return the settler often took along a helpmate in the person of a wife, and if married he returned with his family to face the hardships of a new land, but to own a home. A characteristic of the early settlers was the number of young couples setting out to make a home for themselves in the " Queen's Bush." For the aged the hardships of a new country were too great to be lightly undertaken.

The boon companion of the first settlers was the patient and enduring ox. Amongst stumps, roots and trees his labour was more efficient than that of the more delicate and high-strung nature of the horse. The first clearings were made and the first tillage done by these patient animals. And what a soil it was in those first years! What wheat and what potatoes its black soil gave forth! Yields of 50 and 60 and 70 bushels of wheat per acre were common and endured for many years. But with the passing years some ingredient of the soil which went to the formation of spring wheat vanished and such grain failed to yield, compelling the settler in later years to cultivate fall wheat.

The settler's first object was to live, and only after much and hard labour was this possible. Rough clearings were made, and fields of a kind filled with stumps, piles of stones and brush were sown to grain.

CHAPTER II.

THE SCHOOLMASTER.

In the year 1851, S.S. No. —, in the township of Woolwich, Waterloo County, was built of logs. It had been built upon the "blind line" to accommodate the

LOG SCHOOL HOUSE.

children of neighbouring concessions. Neither concession settlers would consent to the other having the school house built upon its line.

Its walls were of hewn logs, dressed upon one side only and notched and dovetailed at the corners, and the whole covered with split shingles. It faced west and had two main doorways—one, the south, for the boys; the other, the north, for the girls. Its oblong interior was subdivided about ten feet from the entrance by a transverse partition running across the school, which was again subdivided by a central partition, making two ante-rooms. These ante-rooms, with shelving and hooks, served the double purpose of holding the scholars' wraps and caps and lunch baskets or small pails.

Two doorways served as egress to the main body of the school. On entering this main body, to the right and left were two rows of seats and desks flanking a central aisle which led to the master's desk at the far end of the school. Opposite the master's desk at the entrance to the centre aisle was the large " Black Giant " box stove—which could accommodate a 4-foot cordwood stick with ease—used in heating the building in winter.

The rows of seats to the right of the centre aisle were for the boys, those to the left were for the girls. In those seats to the right and left the scholars were graded as to size and age. The smaller tots A, B, C, class— sat in the front seats nearest the master, while further back the pupils increased in size—those in the First Book coming next—succeeded by those of the Second and Third Book, while the older and more advanced pupils—those of the Fourth and Fifth Classes—occupied the end seats farthest from the master's desk.

At the end of the school farthest from the entrance was a raised floor or platform running across the school and of a depth of about ten feet, access to which was by means of two steps. Upon this platform the master's desk was placed with an armchair, while behind this, on the end wall of the school, was a large home-made blackboard.

A few maps, including one of Upper Canada, one of North America and one of Europe, completed the equipment of the school. The windows were small, unshaded and furnished but a poor light. The walls and ceilings were plastered and white-washed. In those days no Board of School Trustees nor finical Medical Health Officer thought of reducing the glare of those white-washed walls to a neutral tint for the budding Newtons and Galileos whose days were spent in study amongst them.

School days! The happiest days of life! Days dear to the heart! Days of sunshine and of tempest— of comedies, sorrows, trials and tragedies, but beyond all the joy time of life! And the playmates of our school days, where are they? Gone! Gone! Long ago! They grew to manhood and womanhood and scattered long ago. Around the old log school scenes were enacted which shall live in memory as long as life shall last.

> " The smiles, the tears, of boyhood's years,
>   The words of love then spoken,
>   The eyes that shone, now dimmed and gone,
>   The many hearts now broken."

Ask the prairies of the West or that western land whose shores are bathed by the blue waters of the Pacific. Many have vanished to the great south land, and some, alas! sleep the sleep that knows no waking. In the old churchyard, hard by the old log school, are some mounds and fallen stone, and here lies much that once was so alluring and of bright promise yet to be, and now, alas! crumbled into dust.

The teacher of the Log School in Woolwich at the

time of which we write was Henry M. Gamble. He was a Canadian by birth, but of Scotch parentage. He was a man of 40 years of age, tall and well-formed, extremely strict, against the use of liquor and false-hoods. Being poor, in adolescent years he learned the trade of carpenter, a calling in much demand in a new country. He followed this trade for a few years, but developing a taste for study in his spare time he thus improved himself, until finally, journeying to the county town at Berlin, he submitted himself to an examination before the Public School Inspector and became a teacher.

His was a thorough nature. Everything he did was done with the most painstaking care. He hated liquor, drunkenness and lying. His one great fault was that his hatred of liquor made his even-handed justice in school discipline lop-sided in dealing with children whose parents were in the liquor trade or hotels. For instance, Tom Ouvrier, whose aunt kept hotel at the neighbouring village half a mile away, and she kept it well, being averse to " boozers," and whose table was celebrated for its good things all over the township : if ever poor Tom was haled to the platform for some boyish delinquency he was always punished more severely than the other boys. The punishment was meted out with grimness and venom, sometimes with the admonition " No bar-room tricks here." Poor Tom ! He has long since fallen into corpulency and operates a commission house in a Canadian city.

Gamble was a good teacher. Friday afternoons were always given over to competition amongst the scholars in the subjects taught. One of the most important of these was spelling. To be able to read and spell English correctly was regarded by the settler as one of the chief

points in an education. Sides were chosen by the
teacher—a big boy and a big girl—as captains of the
opposing sides. These stood against the wall on either
side of the school. The girl captain was given first
choice, and selected from amongst the seated scholars
the one she deemed the best speller. The boy captain
then made a similar selection. Each pupil, on the
name being called out, arose and ranged alongside the
captain who had called. When all of the third and
fourth classes had been selected and ranged along
either wall the contest began.

A mis-spelled word resulted in the pupil uttering it to
take a seat and be out of the contest.

The master gave out the words from the old Spelling
Book—the series of national school books issued by
the Council of Public Instruction of Upper Canada—
or the Readers.

At first words of one or two syllables were given out:
receive and achieve; bread and breadth; deaf and
death; advice and advise; cease and seize; dice and
dies; rice and rise; ant and aunt; chase and chaise; hiss
and his. As these failed to deplete the ranks very much,
longer and more difficult words were given: champagne, indefeasible, guillotine, ingenuousness, naphtha,
nonagenarian, schismatic, shrievalty, surcingle, ter-
giversation, &c. Caoutchouc usually mowed down
three or four spellers. When it didn't, such words as
gubernatorial or phthisicky or threnody would do
the trick.

By the time these words had all been given out the
opposing sides would usually dwindle to one or two.
When the master had given out all his words, the side
having the most spellers standing was declared the
winner. Sometimes the match was declared a draw.

After spelling came arithmetic. The candidates were arranged in a row along the end of the school farthest from the master's desk, with slates ready and pencils poised. The master, placing his armchair in front of the desk, ascended the platform and gave out the questions. First came a long sum in simple addition, with rows of half a dozen figures and columns of the same number. Then the pencils flew until completed, and then began a wild race down the centre aisle to be first to deposit the slate, with the candidate's name written below, face downwards upon the master's chair. In this competition some were slow and others fast. It was a test of accuracy in adding and activity—of body and mind as it were. One girl—big Dick's Harriet—a girl of fifteen years, was conspicuous for her counting in these contests. She was a flying windmill of arms, hands and tongue in counting and of legs in her rush to the master's chair.

Compound addition—£ s. d.; compound subtraction and multiplication were next given, and then followed fractions and proportion and exchange for the more advanced pupils.

Then came questions in geography. In teaching geography Gamble had a method all his own, and withal a very educative one. He would arrange all the pupils of the school in two rows before the blackboard, over which the map was hung, the larger scholars standing on the floor, while the smaller children stood behind them mounted on benches.

With a map showing the counties of Upper Canada, the master took a pointer and, beginning at the head of Lake Erie, would point and call out the counties bordering thereon, while the children in unison and in a sing-song voice named them—Essex, Kent, Elgin,

Norfolk, Haldimand, Monk Welland. The master's object was evidently to name the counties on the outskirts of Upper Canada and then wind up in the centre of the province. For Lincoln, Wentworth, Halton, Peel, York would again be chanted in unison. Then Simcoe, Grey, Bruce, Huron, Lambton, Middlesex, Oxford, Brant, Perth, Waterloo, Wellington. In later lessons the counties east of Toronto would be given. This was an effective way—by ear and eye—of teaching the child geography.

Then followed grammar. In every school are oddly-behaved children. Some are different. They are out of the general run of scholars in behaviour, deportment and speech. An euphemistic term is usually used to describe them when they are called eccentric.

One such in S.S. No. — was Davie Baxter. Davie was a lad of 15 years, with the growth of a man of 21 years. He was big, raw-boned and heavy; slow in his movements and mental processes. He was the son of Scotch parents and attended school only during the winter months. At examination time, when Master Gamble wished to amuse the visitors to the school, he always called up the grammar class, and would ask Davie how many parts there were in grammar. "Four, sir," Davie would reply. "Name them!" cried the master.

"Orthoograaphy,
    Entymoology, Swinetax and Prosodoody,"
Davie would reply amidst a general titter of the whole school.

CHAPTER III.

Boy and Girl.

Amongst the large scholars and most advanced pupils in S.S. No. — in the winter of 1850-1 were Alice Guy and Mary Beaumont; George Gordon and his sister Mary; Jack Haag and Charley Champagne; Stephen Neubecker and his two sisters, Lena and Rosie; Larry Duffy and the two Stewart girls, Katie and Margaret, and their brother George.

These were all pretty much of an age, only a few years separating the oldest from the youngest, all budding into manhood and womanhood. They formed a set of their own. All were in the same classes or studies, and pursued the same pleasures at intermission.

Alice Beaumont at that time was 17 years of age, tall and slim, with dark-brown eyes, an aquiline nose and clear-cut features, and a delicate bloom on either cheek; dark-brown hair, and with small hands and feet. She was shy, modest and good-hearted; always willing to help class-mates in their studies; not quick to anger; always sunny in disposition, never down-hearted.

Her sister Mary was her opposite in many respects. She was short and chunky, with blue eyes and reddish hair; she was quick to anger, impulsive, quick to hate, but also quick to forgive. In this she resembled her brother Guy. Guy Beaumont was a young man of 19 years of age, thick-set, active and vigorous.

Jack Haag and Stephen Neubecker were the sons of neighbouring settlers and were young men in their teens. The former was 18 years of age, of medium stature, dark hair and eyes of a somewhat swarthy complexion, very quick-tempered and inclined to roughness, quick to love and quick to hate. He led in everything where daring was an asset, and was somewhat of a bully; given also to swearing and chewed tobacco. Stephen Neubecker, on the contrary, was mildness personified. He had blue eyes, a fair complexion and light hair. He never engaged in quarrels and was a peacemaker. Stephen was a plodder, slow and sure— by main strength as it were. Knowledge seeped into his head from his studies, while Jack Haag was a brilliant scholar; one review of a subject and he seemed to be its master. He was good in mathematics—which was Stephen's bane—and also a good essayist, and in a pupil this is unusual. He excelled in grammar and composition. Haag had many parts in his nature which were good and others which were the opposite. There seemed to be a continuous struggle going on within him between these two natures. Sometimes one controlled, but oftener the other and baser.

George Gordon was the son of Irish parents and was of average ability. He was tall and slim of stature, kind and generous to a fault, and was a good student.

George and Steve were both favourites with Alice Beaumont. Whenever she was captain of a spelling match she always selected one or other to her side if available.

Larry Duffy was the son of Irish parents, who had but a year or two previous emigrated from the Green Isle to try their fortunes in that part of Upper Canada. Larry was a stout lad of 16 years, of a jolly and good-natured disposition, with red cheeks, grey eyes and reddish hair, and had brought to America with him a "brogue" as rich and rare as any that had ever left the "old sod." Because he was a "greenhorn" the other boys at school frequently made game of him—sent him on wild goose chases or fruitless errands.

One day on a visit to the water-pail for a drink little Jimmy John Ross, who sat immediately behind Larry, placed a bent pin on Duffy's seat. The latter had scarcely sat down, when with a screech that electrified the whole school, he went heavenwards, frantically grabbing at his posterior where the pin was imbedded in the flesh. "Duffy to the desk!" roared the master. On reaching the desk Duffy—who was just learning his A, B, C.'s—kept rubbing and twisting as if endeavouring to see the affected part, while the remainder of the school was convulsed. "What do you mean by such conduct, Duffy?" cried the master. "Plaze, sir, the byes do be makin' bad discoorse wid me!" replied Duffy, still rubbing the seat of affliction. "Who did it?" asked the master. "Sorrow the one o' me knows, yer honner! The runions do be always tazin me!" replied the harassed Irish lad. "Take your seat, sir, and go on with your lessons!" called the master.

Duffy returned to his seat, glaring around as he did so, in an endeavour to discover the culprit who had caused him such torture, and carefully rubbed off the seat with his coat tails before sitting down to avoid any more bent pins.

The Stewarts were twins; they were 16 years of age; both were brunettes. Katie had an impediment in her speech and stuttered. Asked one day in class to define "nail," she replied: "A horny excresenths on the endths of the fingersth and thumbths and toeths." Her sister, Margaret Stewart, was of a jolly and good-natured disposition, and was a good student.

Charley Champagne was of French extraction. He was big for his age—15 years—being 6 ft. tall, rough and raw-boned, with high cheek-bones, black hair and eyes, and of a sluggish nature. His speech was broken English. He was greatly given to sleep. Frequently at intermissions he would select a cosy corner of the school yard in favourable weather and fall asleep, and not hearing the warning bell, would sometimes not wake up for an hour after school was called, and then would walk sheepishly in amidst the amused glances of the whole school.

In the matter of punishment, the rawhide whip and the tawse (a long leather strap split into strips) were the only instruments used for punishment by Master Gamble. His predecessor in the school—a man named Fitzpatrick—had been noted for his floggings. For this punishment a stout lad was chosen, whose shoulders had to be mounted by the culprit, and whose wrists had to be firmly grasped by the mounter. Then with beech gads the master laid on with vigour upon the back and buttocks of the victim until fatigue or the giving out of the beech gads called a halt to the proceedings.

Strange to say, in those early days both parents and trustees were firmly of the opinion—chiefly, I suppose, because in their own schooldays they had undergone similar forms of education—that knowledge was chiefly instilled by the gad. So much was this the case that trustees would, if possible, hire a teacher only who had a reputation for giving "sound thrashings." But Master Gamble had a different way. By precept, example, kindness and heart-to-heart talks he induced good behaviour in the school and reduced punishments to a minimum, and brought about such a desire

2

to study upon the part of the scholars that his school, S.S. No. —, was the most advanced of any in the township, and was so termed by the inspector.

CHAPTER IV.

The Rivals.

ALICE BEAUMONT did not lack admirers. Jack Haag, Stephen Neubecker and George Gordon, all were anxious to stand well in her esteem. Alice, though friendly with all, did not show any special predilection for anybody. She was always intent on her studies. She was friendly to all overtures, but was ever anxious to utilize her school days to their utmost.

Jack Haag, whose general proficiency was by far the best in the school, offered and frequently helped her in difficult questions in arithmetic and algebra, this last a subject which the elder scholars in the school had but recently taken up that winter. In this position as mentor Jack Haag endeavoured to ingratiate himself into Alice's good graces. She was grateful for his help, and showed it by words and a kindly countenance, but further she did not go. There was a line beyond which no one could pass.

At length the time of the yearly school entertainment came around. This was an annual exhibition of the capabilities of the scholars to the school section by means of declamations, recitations, songs and music— in groups and singly—and dialogues instituted by Master Gamble during his occupancy as teacher. It was always looked forward to by the whole school section, as well as by the scholars themselves, with keen anticipation.

The entertainment was usually held towards the end of February or beginning of March, and for a month previous there was always a general relaxation in the discipline of the school. Studies were not relaxed, but greater vigour and efficiency was marked in order that they might be gotten through with and the engrossing subjects of the entertainment proceeded with. At 4 o'clock, when the school was dismissed for the day, the big boys and girls would hold a general consultation and discuss duets, dialogues and recitations and allot parts, ways and means for stage settings, lighting and decorating the school at the coming concert.

For a month previous to the performance a neighbouring farmer, an old man, note perfect in music and an admirable player on the 'cello or bass fiddle, named Jno. Haw, was yearly impressed into service, and came twice weekly with his big bass fiddle to conduct practice for the musical part of the entertainment. He usually appeared shortly after 3 p.m., and sharp on the dismissal of the school led off the music, his bass fiddle resting on the master's chair, while surrounded by a bevy of the big girls—and small ones, too—and these last by the big boys, he led off in song.

He was of a religious turn of mind, so that his numbers were mostly hymns: "The Sweet Bye and Bye," "Jesus, Lover of my Soul," "Title Clear," "Nearer my God to Thee," "Rock of Ages," "Oh! what shall the Harvest be?" "Onward, Christian Soldiers," "Safe in the Arms of Jesus," &c.

The sight of this old man—he was approaching 75 years of age—surrounded by a group of scholars in the heyday of their youth, his head thrown back, his mouth wide open singing, disclosing bare gums without a tooth, giving the pitch of the notes, and with his gray hair falling backwards from his head in a shaggy tuft, while at the same time he drew the bow—across the strings with each note—was one long to be remembered by the scholars of old No. —. Those were the great schooldays of winter.

First the school was decorated. Huge piles of evergreens were brought by the boys from the neighbouring forest, and the big girls cut out pasteboard lettering, upon which were sewn the evergreens. These formed mottoes, which were nailed to the walls and above the windows. These mottoes were the old copybook virtues: "Welcome!" "There's no Royal Road to Learning!" "Labor omnia vincit!" "It's never too late to mend!" Wreaths of evergreens also were attached around windows and doors. A platform was erected, extending across the end of the school for a stage, with draw curtain and dressing rooms on either side.

At length the great day arrived. School was held only in the forenoon, the afternoon being devoted to giving the finishing touches to the surroundings. Shortly after 6 o'clock the cutters and sleigh loads of people began arriving. By 7 o'clock the school was packed to the doors. The school was lighted by many oil lamps with reflectors attached to the walls. Everyone was on the qui vive. The girls in their white dresses, the boys looking uncomfortable in their new Sunday suits.

Promptly at 7.30 o'clock the master, Mr. Gamble, ascended the platform and informed the assembled people that because of the lengthy programme they must begin the entertainment at once and called the first number on the

PROGRAMME.

1. The Choir: "In the Sweet Bye and Bye!"—by the whole school. This event was led off by Mr. Haw and his bass fiddle, the fine pitch of the ladies' voices mingling well with the hoarse bass of the big boys' voices and passed off well, and was applauded, and for encore gave:

2. "What shall the Harvest be?"—by Choir. This was followed by:

3. A Recitation: "Lord Uhlin's Daughter"—by Jack Haag. This was well declaimed. Haag had a good voice and presence, and when finished his effort was applauded. Then came:

4. Song: "Come back to Erin!"—by Mary Gordon, which was well rendered, and for an encore she gave:

5. "The Harp that once through Tara's Halls!" This was followed by

6. The Choir: "Title Clear!" which was followed by

7. A Recitation: "Afar in the Desert!"—by Margaret Stewart. Then came:

8. A Song: "Ben Bolt!"—by Jack Haag.

   "O! do you remember sweet Alice Ben Bolt,
      Sweet Alice, whose hair was so brown,
   Who wept with delight when you gave her a
      smile,
   And trembled with fear at your frown?"

   Haag had a splendid voice and a good range, and on finishing "Ben Bolt" was enthusiastically applauded. For encore he gave:

9. "The prettiest girl I ever saw!"

   "Oh! The prettiest girl I ever saw! I ever saw!
      Was sucking cider through a straw,
                I-oh! I-oh! I-oh!"

Then came :

10. A Recitation : " The Coral Grove !"—by Rosie Neubecker. This was followed by

11. The Choir : " Jesus, Lover of my Soul," which was followed by :

12. A Song : " Annie Laurie !"—by a quartette composed of Alice, Mary and Guy Beaumont and George Gordon. The piece was enthusiastically applauded, and for encore the same quartette gave :

13. " Will ye no come back again ?" This was followed by

14. A Recitation : " The Slave's Dream"—by Alice Beaumont. Dressed all in white, with a distinguished appearance and in a clear voice, she repeated Longfellow's undying poem : " The Slave's Dream " :

> " Beside the ungathered rice he lay,
>   His sickle in his hand,
>   His breast was bare, his matted hair
>   Was buried in the sand,
>   And through the mist and shadow of sleep
>   He saw his native land !"

and was heartily applauded. Then followed :

15. The Choir : " Marching through Georgia !" Then came

16. A Comic Song : " Poor Yacob !"—by Stephen Neubecker. Dressed for the part with wooden shoes, wool stockings reaching to the knees, knee breeches, a cutaway coat with brass buttons, high vest, cap and stick and bundle in a red bandanna handkerchief over his shoulder, a typical German emigrant, Stephen entered the stage and, after bowing, sang :

" I am schust coming over to dis countree,
 Und 'twas better if I tole you before right
  avay,
 Und I dinks it vas a humbug und a
  schwindle,
 In dis countree vat dey calls Amerikay.
 I leaves behind mine fader and mine moder,
 In Deutschland a couple of months or dree,
 Und I takes me to de steamboat ship a ticket,
 And I sails across de salty vater sea!"

The song was well delivered. The appearance typical, so that when Steve finished he was vociferously applauded. For encore he gave

17. A Song: " Lauterbach."

 " In Lauterbach habe Ich ein Strumpf ver-
  loren,
 Und ohne Strumpf geh Ich nicht Heim,
 Dann gehr Ich gleich wieder nach Lauter-
  bach zu
 Und Kauf mier ein Strumpf ans Bein!"

Very few of the audience understood German, so that Steve was allowed to retire, but with a measure of applause.

The next number was

18. A Duet: " When ye gang awa', Jamie!"—by Alice Beaumont and George Gordon. This was exceedingly well rendered, with 'cello accompaniment, the fine soprano voice of Miss Beaumont contrasting well with the rich baritone of George Gordon.

In the preparation of this number the song had caused some heart-burnings. When the duet was first suggested by Margaret Stewart, she had mentioned the names of Alice Beaumont and Jack

Haag as the singers, and those names were set down on the preliminary programme, but when practice came to be taken up, Alice Beaumont absolutely refused to sing it with Haag. Her reason was, she didn't think she could do the song justice. Finally, after some coaxing, and when George Gordon himself asked her to sing it, she finally consented on condition his was to be the male voice. This, of course, was told Jack Haag, who took mortal offence thereat. As an encore Miss Alice and George gave :

19. "Loch Lomond." Then followed

20. A Recitation : "The Well of St. Keyne !"—by Mary Beaumont. Then came

21. The Choir : "Nearer my God to Thee !" After which came a quartette :

22. Song : "I'll take you home again, Kathleen !"—by Mary Gordon and Mary Beaumont, and Katie and Margaret Stewart, and for encore Mary Gordon sang—

23. Song : "Kathleen Mavourneen !" Then came

24. The Choir : "Onward, Christian Soldiers !" After which came

25. A Coon Song : "Old Black Joe !"—by Guy Beaumont. Guy was blackened up to represent a negro, with high-water collar, cutaway black coat and striped pants, and rendered his piece very well leaning on a walking stick. To repeated applause he gave

26. A Song : "My old Kentucky Home !" Then followed

27. A Dialogue : "The Merchant of Venice "—with Guy Beaumont as Shylock and Jack Haag as

Portia. This was well acted and drew vigorous applause. Then came

28. A Song: "When you and I were young, Maggie!" by George Gordon. Possessing a fine baritone voice, George rendered this old song exceptionally well and was enthusiastically applauded. For encore he gave:

29. "Listen to the Mocking Bird!" This brought the programme to a close. The teacher mounted the platform and thanked the assembled people for their attendance and attention. The Choir then sang

30. "God Save the Queen!"

The gathering then dispersed to their homes, with many comments of praise for the proficiency and ability of the scholars of old S.S. No. —.

CHAPTER V.

THE GARAFRAXA ROAD.

THE Garafraxa Road—the eastern highway for entrance to "The Queen's Bush," and many a ton of freight passed over its surface in settlers' effects, and many a poor settler remembered with poignant sorrow its swamps and corduroy—extended from Fergus, in Wellington County, in the south—12 miles north of Guelph—to the townsite of Sydenham, on the shores of the southern extremity of Owen Sound, an arm of the Georgian Bay.

This highway had been opened as a colonization road by the Government of Upper Canada in the year 1839. Its survey was given over to Charles Rankin, P.L.S., and he was given a free hand in laying out its route and with instructions to lay out a townsite at its northern extremity, where it touched the waters of the Georgian Bay—christened Sydenham, later changed to Owen Sound.

The road had many deviations, due to following the high land and hardwood timber, and thus avoiding swamps and the building of "corduroy" causeways. The road was so called because of its origin in the township of West Garafraxa in the County of Wellington. Fergus itself lay on the boundary between that township and Nichol township.

After leaving Fergus the road ran north-westerly 12 miles to the village of Arthur, located at the junction of four townships—Peel, West Garafraxa, Arthur and West Luther. Then, still trending to the north-west, it ran through the township of Arthur for another 12 miles to the village of Mount Forest in the north-west corner of Arthur township, thence running almost due north for about 50 miles, striking the waters of the Georgian Bay at the townsite of Sydenham. Up to Mount Forest the road was in Wellington County, but after passing this point it entered the County of Grey, running between the townships of Egremont, Glenelg, Holland and Sydenham on the east, and Normanby, Bentinck, Sullivan and Derby on the west.

The giving of free grants of land of 50 acres each on both sides of this road, after its survey, in the above-named townships led to the early clearing of the land adjacent to the highway, but further back all was virgin forest.

At Durham, 17 miles north of Mount Forest, a Government colonization road had been surveyed west-wards to Bucks Crossing on the Saugeen River in August, 1848, and later was extended on westwards to Penetangore, on the shores of Lake Huron.

The building of the Garafraxa Road (and the same may be said of the Durham Road) was let by the Government of Upper Canada in sections of $\frac{1}{2}$, 1, 1$\frac{1}{2}$ and 2-mile stretches; where swamps were encountered the minimum length was given out; where good timber and high land occurred longer mileage was contracted for. The road was surveyed 1 chain (66 ft.) in width and was cleared of timber, but all stumps, excepting those interfering with making the road passable, were allowed to stand. Causeways of logs were laid across swamps and streams to make the road passable for wheeled vehicles. As before mentioned, double rows of 50-acre lots on each side of the road were given as free grants to settlers.

The regulations of these free grants required these settlers to be subjects of Queen Victoria, males, and over the age of 18 years. Twelve acres of land had to be cleared in four years, counting from the 1st of January, following the taking up of the land. When chopping and logging, 5 acres of bush was looked upon as a fair winter's work; 3 acres could not be deemed excessive in the same time. Persons so taking up land had to be capable of maintaining themselves until such time as the land was self-supporting. If a lot was abandoned by a settler the same was to be open for sale or grant to another. Settlers on receiving a free grant had the privilege of purchasing, in addition, sufficient to make up 200 acres of land. The settler, on going to the Land Office, received a Location Ticket from the Crown Land Agent, after first giving his name, age, condition, trade or profession; whether married or single, and if married the name of his wife, the number of children, and their names and ages; where he was from and the township in which he wished to settle, with a certificate of good character from a clergyman.

On receiving his Location Ticket the settler was required to take possession of his lot within 30 days after the ticket was issued, and put in a state of cultivation at least 12 acres of land in the course of the following 4 years; to build a house at least 18 × 24 ft., and to reside on the lot until the conditions of settlement were fulfilled, and then a title was issued for the property by the Crown.

Leave was granted the settler to purchase three other additional 50-acre lots at 8 shillings ($2.00) per acre.

The timber on the land was reserved by the Govern‚ ment, except that for the clearings, until the land had been paid for and a Patent issued, and to be subject to any general timber duty thereafter. The Location Ticket was not assignable without permission of the Crown Lands Agent. The License of occupation to be null and void unless all the conditions of settlement were fulfilled, and not more than 200 acres were to be sold to any one person upon those terms.

On applying for a Location Ticket, the Crown Lands Agent gave the applicant a list of lots not already taken up. This list did not contain many lots, and was drawn out, as far as possible, with a view to prevent any two men inspecting and selecting the same lot. The Agent also planned to have people of a congenial type settle in the same locality.

As before mentioned, the whole of the road was chopped to a width of 66 feet; all trees 8 inches in diameter and under were cut close to the ground. The whole of the timber on the road allowance was cut into logging lengths—12-14 ft., and these, together with all brushwood and rubbish, were piled on each side of the road, that later, when dry, it might be burned, so leaving a span 45 feet in width in the middle of the allowance for a roadway. Timber might be felled into the woods on either side, but not into the clearings!

In swamps and where causewaying was required the whole of the timber had to be cut close to the ground for a width of 20 feet in the centre of the road. Causewaying was made of straight sound logs, laid evenly and close together and at right angles to the roadway, and each log had to be 16 feet long. All bridges of 15-feet span and under were included under the head of causewaying. Contracts for chopping and logging the road varied from 23 pounds sterling to 25 pounds sterling per mile, and causewaying from 7s. 6d. to 10s. per rod.

So that we see the Garafraxa Road has a history extending back for more than 80 years—reaching out into that dim past of which the oldest settler has only a misty memory. Over the lonely forest trail or "blaze" made by Surveyor Rankin in 1839, some of the early settlers of Owen Sound penetrated in the summer of 1840, and for more than 40 years after this it was the highway to the new lands of "The Queen's Bush."

CHAPTER VI.

THE PIONEERS.

THE Pioneers of Grey and Bruce pierced the "Bush" with roadways for settlement; cleared the forest; built schools, churches and grist mills and helped form the various municipalities. They laboured with an enthusiasm, fortitude and industry that finally overcame all obstacles. After many weary months of toil at underbrushing, chopping, logging and clearing, they finally brought the land into a condition to produce something upon which they could subsist. Miles and miles of forest lay between them and the most ordinary comforts of civilized life, and over those long difficult and weary miles every pound of the necessary supplies of food had to be carried.

The prospective settler, dissatisfied with the outlook, or lack of opportunity, in the older and more settled parts of the Province of Upper Canada, left an outpost of civilization "down below" and started out into the "Bush" in search of a location, on which to settle, clear a few acres of land, erect a shanty and thereby establish a "squatter's" right to the lot of his choice.

In the process, the pioneer underwent many hardships. Before leaving civilization he carefully prepared the pack he had to carry and subsist upon. This comprised a supply of provisions sufficiently large to last him during his stay in the "Bush"—flour, baking powder, salt, tea, sugar and bacon, which with cooking and eating utensils —a frying pan, knife, fork, tin-cup and plate, spoon, an auger and chisel and matches, rolled in a stout blanket, was carried on the back by means of pack straps carried around each shoulder and occasionally from the forehead. Thus equipped and with axe and gun he faced the wilderness.

After tramping many a weary mile through the forest, following a Surveyor's "blaze," a spot appealing to his ideal was arrived at. He might note the land was covered with heavy hardwood timber—a sure indication of a good soil—and if a spring of cool clear water occurred hard by, so much the better, and his resolution to locate there was quickly made. Caching his provisions from rain and wild animals in some hollow tree, he would proceed to make a clearing by underbrushing and felling trees.

The fallen trees were cut into suitable lengths, and, notching each one for the corner, he began the building of his shanty. After much hard labour this was erected —a poor backwoodsman's hut at its best—an opening made for a doorway and a small one as a window to admit light. The door was of planks made from split cedar blocks; while the roof was covered with hemlock or elm bark or of split cedar shingles.

The spaces between the logs were filled with triangular pieces of cedar (chinking) and moss and plastered over with clay. In a corner of the interior, a bed of hemlock boughs was placed. A table was made by driving four crotched sticks into the earthen floor, upon which rested, supported by cross pieces, a couple of split planks. For seats, blocks of wood had to serve. The cooking consisted mainly of scones—flour, baking powder and salt, mixed with water and cooked in a frying pan.

As time went on, the settler continued the felling of

trees to enlarge his clearing until finally want of provisions compelled him to again visit the "front" for a fresh supply.

Such a life was lonely in the extreme, the settler's only visitor being an occasional Indian in the pursuit of the chase. The howling of the wolves through the night often sent its thrill through the cabin home of the settler, or the forages of Bruin in search of meats or sweets in the log home of the pioneer.

A source of great irritation to the early settler was the destruction caused by the coming of deer in the night to browse upon the growing wheat. On rising at daybreak and throwing open his door, the settler would frequently see a troop of deer quietly browsing in his young grain. A shout and they quickly scampered off to disappear into the surrounding forest.

CHAPTER VII.

"To the Saugeen!" (Chippeway Sajin—Mouth of River).

"To the Saugeen!" "To the Saugeen!" was the cry that spread through the older parts of the Province of Upper Canada in 1850.

Tales told by returned prospectors of the heavy timber, the excellent soil, the good water—all to be had in free grants, in the wilderness north of the Huron Tract—were in every mouth, and all for the taking!

Access to the Saugeen Country was in two directions. One on the east—the Garafraxa Road, running from Fergus to Owen Sound—and the other by means of the Great Lake to the westwards, by boat during summer or upon the shore ice in winter.

John Beaumont was a small farmer in Woolwich Township, Waterloo County, and had long fought an unequal battle with circumstances over which he had no control. His holding was small, comprising only 50 acres, and though not poor land, still there was a dearth of water upon it. No streams ran through or near it, and though well after well had been sunk upon it, only small quantities of water were obtained, which scarce sufficed, in dry seasons, to supply the farm wants. This, together with a desire to secure more land, not only for himself but for his sons, made him turn his thoughts to the Saugeen country. A hasty trip over the Garafraxa Road to Bentinck (now Durham) in the Fall of 1850 and westwards into Brant Township, convinced him that there good lands were to be had for the taking. The following winter he made preparations to move to the "bush" by selling his land and such stock and implements as he would not require in his new home—retaining 2 yoke of oxen and 2 wagons to transport his family, farming implements and household goods northwards.

We see him, then, setting out in the early spring of 1851, with his two ox-teams, loaded with his family and all his worldly goods, trekking eastwards across Pilkington and Nichol Townships, in Wellington County, to Fergus, where the road began which would lead him to his Eldorado. He reached Fergus on the evening of the first day out and put up at the comfortable old Wellington Hotel—a notable stone hostelry in the early days.

Fergus, at that early date, was a compact town of many substantial buildings. The houses and business places were mostly built of stone and the surrounding farming country fairly well settled.

The next morning after breakfast a start was made northwards. Mr. Beaumont, on foot, with his ox goad, directing the leading ox team with its wagon piled high with household goods and Mrs. Beaumont and Mary ensconced in their midst. The second ox team was driven by Guy, with Alice, Alex and Jack on the wagon, with the remainder of the goods and chattels.

Towards midday they arrived at the banks of a spring creek crossing the roadway, over which a bridge had been thrown. As the animals were tired with the heavy pull over miry roads, Beaumont called for a halt for dinner. A fire was made by the roadside, kettles and pans brought out and preparations made for the midday meal. Guy and Alex outspanned the oxen and gave them some bundles of hay from one of the wagons.

In the meantime, Mrs. Beaumont had gotten out one

of her hams from the wagon, which she took to a near-by
stump on the roadway, but close to the surrounding
forest, cut off a number of slices sufficient for all the
members of the party and took them to the fire which
Jack and Alex had built, and began frying them.

During this time, Alice had gone to one of the wagons,
busily engaged in unpacking dishes, cups and saucers,

BEAR AND HAM.

when happening to glance up she uttered a loud scream,
crying " Oh, mamma ! A big black dog is eating your
ham ! "

Mrs. Beaumont turned and seeing a black animal at
the stump eating her ham, grabbed a stick and rushed
upon him, striking him a couple of smart blows upon the
nose. The animal uttered a low growl and rising on his

hind legs, rushed forwards to grasp the woman in his powerful fore-paws. The now terrified woman screamed, turned and fled towards the wagons—with the bear, for such it was, in swift pursuit!

But other help was at hand. At the first scream uttered by Alice, John Beaumont and Guy had grasped their muskets from the wagons and simultaneously two shots rang out and Master Bruin was halted in his career. Two more shots brought him to the ground, where he was quickly despatched by a shot behind the fore-leg. Mrs. Beaumont then fainted after all the danger was past.

On Alice chafing her hands and wetting her face with a handkerchief dipped in cold water, she came to, but shuddered as she saw the bear lying dead a few yards away.

"Well, mother! Your dog was a pretty big one!" said John Beaumont. "It was a rash thing to rush at and strike a bear with a stick!"

"Oh my!" exclaimed his wife, pressing her hand against her heart, "Was it a bear? And I thought it a big dog! I shall never forget his fierce teeth and awful mouth as he rushed at me after I struck him on the nose!"

"Yes! Bears are quick-tempered brutes" said her husband, "and fiercely resent blows. No doubt the scent of the bacon attracted him from the woods to your stump. In future, better leave all your meat at the wagons."

The party then turned to and had their midday meal, when after an hour's rest for the animals they were again inspanned and the journey northwards resumed.

Towards evening they came upon an unusual sight. They had arrived at a small spring creek, flowing over a gravelly bottom and with water not more than 4 or 5 inches in depth. The stream was probably three or four yards wide and flowing to the westwards and was no doubt one of the streams that formed the head waters of the Conestogo River—one of the main tributaries of the Grand River and emptying into Lake Erie.

Some previous traveller—perhaps in order to pass over dry shod—had cut down small cedar limbs, half as thick as one's arm and 5 or 6 ft. long, and enough of these had been piled upon each other and in the stream with their length parallel with the current, to pass over without wetting one's feet, but the remarkable thing was that the stream to the right hand side of the road, for a distance of perhaps 30 feet, where it emerged from the forest, was literally filled with fish from bank to bank!

The fish were of all sizes, and so thick there was scarcely room to flap their tails. An inspection showed them to be "suckers," which had no doubt ascended the stream from the Lake, in early spring, to spawn and had been thus imprisoned—a silvery, squirming, flopping mass—by the cedar causeway, on their return.

A halt was made while several pailfuls were scooped from the stream; heads and tails lopped off, split open and the entrails removed and the interior sprinkled with salt and packed away in tubs for use upon the journey. Some of the cedar limbs were then removed from the causeway to release the fish and the pioneers again resumed their march.

Progress was slow, as the road in many places—due to the frost coming out of the ground—was springy and heavy, so that it was almost nightfall before they reached John Wright's Log Tavern at Arthur.

CHAPTER VIII.

WRIGHT'S TAVERN, ARTHUR.

WRIGHT'S TAVERN, ARTHUR, was a comfortable log building of large size and with commodious rooms. Adjacent thereto were log stables and a log driving shed. A large yard fronted upon the tavern proper.

WRIGHT'S TAVERN.

Over its main doorway hung a large sign with a painting of a bottle and a glass, drawn with rude artistic skill, and a sign—" Here's looking at you !"

On entering the main door, the traveller came into a large room with a huge fireplace—on which a pile of

logs were burning—on one side, and on the other,
facing the doorway, was a high counter—the bar—
behind which, on shelves, were ranged decanters of
various liquors and glasses. Below the shelving were
barrels of whisky and beer.

After stabling the oxen, Mr. Beaumont and the boys
found, on entering the tavern, that a dance was in
progress. The bar-room was filled with men—mostly
young—though some middle-aged men were amongst the
throng, who were evidently from the surrounding settlements. Two men were behind the bar serving drinks
—John Wright, the proprietor, and an assistant, a
Frenchman named Jos. Toranjean.

"Treating" was going on and the hum of many
voices arose while the air was hazy with tobacco smoke.
Two coal oil lamps in brackets, with reflectors, were
attached to the walls of the room and furnished light.

Music was now heard coming from an adjoining room
—which was ordinarily a large dining room, but had
been cleared of its furniture for the dance. The sweet
penetrating notes of the violin were heard accompanied
by the deep "boom" "boom" of the 'cello or bass
fiddle; the taps of boots upon the floor and the swishes
of the ladies' skirts as they whirled about in the mazes of
the dance betokened Terpsichorean jollity.

Seeking out Mrs. Wright in the kitchen, where Mrs.
Beaumont and the girls had already found refuge, Mr.
Beaumont arranged for supper, beds and breakfasts for
the party.

"I am pretty well skimped for rooms with all this
crowd here at the dance," said Mrs. Wright. "Some of
the Bloods, with their ladies, are here from Fergus and
Elora and have engaged all the spare rooms, but I guess
we can manage for you. You can have these two rooms

here off the kitchen—you, Mrs. Beaumont and the two girls can occupy one while Mr. Beaumont and the three boys can occupy the other." " That will do fine," said Mr. Beaumont; " one of the boys can sleep on the floor! A shakedown is no hardship!" and so it was arranged.

A supper of wild duck, venison, bread, butter, fried potatoes, hot coffee and custard pie was eaten in the kitchen, after which Mrs. Beaumont and the girls, tired after the day's excitement and trip, retired to their room for the night.

Mr. Beaumont and the boys decided to see the dance before retiring. On entering the ball room (or rather dining room) they found gaiety in full swing. Upon a stout table at one end of the room, chairs were placed upon which two musicians—with violin and bass fiddle— were seated, discoursing sweet music.

The violinist was a man of middle age; dark almost to swarthiness, and with a heavy mane of hair descending from his head, and of an unusual physical deportment. At rest, that is, when not engaged in playing his instrument, he appeared like any other mortal, but once he seized his bow and struck the strings an unusual facial contortion followed. His nostrils dilated, his eyes rolled, his head nodded to right and to left to the strains of the music. At every down-stroke of the bow he uttered a snort, at the same time stamping his feet and moving his body keeping time to the tune.

Guy Beaumont gazed at this apparition for some time in wonder and astonishment, and presently said to his father—" Say, dad! That fellow has St. Vitus' Dance."

" Oh, no!" returned the father, " I've heard of him! He's an oddity! He is named Willie Tamson, the fiddler! ' Wandering Willie ' they call him! He fiddles for all the dances in this part of the country!"

The strains of a waltz now struck up and couples were selected and glided away in the mazes of a triple-time tune—the wide hoop skirts of the ladies—which was the mode at that period—ballooning out in the circles of the dance, accompanied by bursts of noise from the doorway leading into the bar-room.

At the completion of the waltz, partners were selected for a " Square Dance." This was a cotillon or quadrille. Each set of the quadrille comprised four couples forming a square, with a couple on each side of the square; a floor manager called out the figures of the dance, which were five in number. The musicians struck up " The girl I left behind me!" and the dance was on :

1st.　　" " Salute your partners." This the gentleman did by bowing to his lady.

2nd.　　" Right hand to partner and left hand to lady on right !" came next.

3rd.　　" Ladies change !" on which each gentleman took the hand of a different lady until the sides of the square had been circled—coming around to his own partner again when—

4th.　　" Balance all !" This was heel and toe dancing by gentleman and lady and was a general " hoe down "; then—

5th.　　" Swing the lady!" This was always entered on with zest—the partners swinging around in a circle with more ballooning of skirts—the floor presenting a mass of skirts with here and there a dark patch where the dark clothing of the men showed fitfully amongst the flying drapery !

The quadrille finished, the musicians struck up a Scotch reel—then a Strathspey followed by clog dancing, in which a couple of young settlers were expert.

In the meantime the noise from the bar-room had increased in volume. Curses and high words were becoming momentarily more audible and Guy Beaumont ran back to see what was afoot.

The bar-room was densely packed with men, who appeared to be divided into two factions—one and the larger was led by a short, dark, thickset man named Thomson—" fighting Bob Thomson!" he was called, who had backed up a young man with blue eyes and fair hair and not more than 19 or 20 years of age and named Jack Lennox, into a corner, at the end of the bar.

As Guy entered the bar-room, Thomson, who was bare-headed and shaking his fist in Lennox's face, exclaimed " You're a coward! And so are all the Lennoxes. I can lick any Lennox that ever lived! I gave your brother Jim a thrashing last Fall he'll remember as long as he lives! Can you fight?" and Thomson flicked the back of his hand into Lennox's face.

" You are an older and a heavier man than I am!" declared Lennox, " but I'm not afraid of you, Thomson! I will fight you and whip you too, but not in this crowded room! Come outside and form a ring, where I can have fair play!"

" That's right! Give the boy a fair show Thomson!" cried several in the crowd.

"I'll give him all the show he wants—more than he wants, if I get my hands upon him!" declared the bruiser. " Come on outside, my young fighting cock, and I will show you."

The crowd now began streaming out of the doorway and on to the roadway. A great circle was formed. The two combatants occupied opposite sides of the circle. Both were stripped to the waist with only trousers on, bareheaded and barefooted for more secure footing.

Thomson, a burly, swarthy and thick-set man was a known "bruiser" and "rough and tumble" fighter and had in past years figured in many fights in which bones had been broken and in one case an eye gouged out—a favourite pastime—and ears and noses bitten off. Some of the crowd, seeing the great disparity

THE FIGHT AT WRIGHT'S TAVERN.

in the build of the men, sickened at the thought of what Thomson would do to Lennox and endeavoured to stop the fight, but Lennox raised his hand and said to his friends " Do not be alarmed. I will show up Thomson for what he is—a bully. He cannot lay a hand on me and I will give him the trimming of his life !"

Lennox was a slim lad of not over 20 years of age, but lithe as a panther and had the previous winter been working in Guelph, where he had taken some lessons in the then new art of " sparring."

Each man had his friends and sympathizers in the crowd.

" Eat up the b - - - - - r, Bob!" exclaimed a roughly clad settler named Bill Curry. " The d - - - n Lennox gang are all yellow dogs! and this one the youngest whelp of the breed! Make him so he will never fight again!"

" Wait until I get my hands on him—the whelp!" said Thomson.

The scene now on the roadway, in front of the old log tavern, was indeed a weird one! The night was starlit but no moon showed. The ring of faces around the combatants was lit up by a number of pine torches held high by some of the onlookers. The two gladiators stripped almost naked upon either side—the black unkempt hair, and heavy hairy chest and heavy and brutal countenance and thick body of Thomson, contrasting vividly with the lithe boyish frame, blue eyes and fair hair of his youthful antagonist, Lennox.

" Don't let him get his hands on you Jack!" exclaimed a sympathizer by the side of Lennox, " or you are a gonner! Keep circling him when he rushes! Let him tire himself out with his rushes and then step in and give it to him!"

" Don't worry! I'll fix him!" declared Lennox. " Are you ready Lennox?" bawled Thomson. " I am ready!" said Lennox. " Then you b - - - - r! I'll have your heart out!" and with a roar like a bull, intended to terrify his antagonist, Thomson rushed forwards, waving his fists.

Lennox took two steps forward when Thomson rushed and with the agility of a panther he ducked under Thomson's guard, and instantly straightening a whack resounded on the air as he plunged his right into Thomson's stomach. It was the modern "solar plexus" blow. Thomson dropped his arms, stopping in mid-career with a grunt and a stare like an animal that had been pole-axed, while Lennox danced away out of danger and began circling for another opening.

"Grab him, Bob! Grab him! The devil don't fight fair! Grab him and gouge out his eyes!" yelled a Thomsonite. But grabbing a circling bounding form was not an easy matter for Thomson. He began to feel here was a new form of fighting, where brute strength was not everything.

Recovering from the stomach blow, he cautiously moved forwards, endeavouring to corner his opponent and come to a clinch, but the latter dashed in and out tapping Thomson on face and nose and once drawing blood from the nose. The blood coursed down his face, giving Thomson a hideous appearance. This brought a roar from the Lennox sympathizers. Angered by the derisive cheers, Thomson sprang forwards with a lunge, receiving two severe blows in the face in so doing, but succeeded in grabbing Lennox by the left arm. Scarcely had he done so when Lennox's right, travelling upwards from the hip and with all his power behind it, struck Thomson on the point of the chin, lifting him off his feet and hurling him backwards to the earth insensible.

This ended the fight. Water was brought and thrown on Thomson's face and breast and presently he came to. He was raised up by his friends and supported to his rig in the driving shed and presently with some of his cronies drove off to his homestead.

Lennox returned to the bar-room, resumed his garments, stood around and chatted for a time and then said he believed he, too, would be going home.

The crowd then thinned out, many leaving to talk for long afterwards how " fighting Bob Thomson " had met his Waterloo.

PROHIBITION.

The dancing still kept up until the wee small hours of morning, but by cock-crow it too had ceased and gradually the inmates of the old log tavern sank to rest.

On rising early the next morning to have an early start, and on going out front, Mr. Beaumont discovered the proprietor, John Wright, at the pump, dousing buckets of cold water on to man lying in the gutter near by.

" Why, Mr. Wright ! What in the world are you doing ? " exclaimed Beaumont.

"I'm cooling off this boozer who has been hanging around my house all night guzzling free drinks!" declared the tavern keeper.

"Who is he?" asked Beaumont.   "He's an old 'souse' named Bow Sisely!" exclaimed Wright, "and I'll cool him off!" and with that he drenched the figure with another bucket of cold water.

Sisely gradually raised himself from the ground, holding up a protesting hand to the tavern keeper. "Misher Wright! I'm a sober man!" he declared. "Ain't a soberer mansh about the place than I am!"

"I'll sober you!" exclaimed Wright and gave him another bucketful.

Sisely unsteadily got to his feet and staggered away out of reach, drenched to the skin and with his garments streaming water at every step.

CHAPTER IX.

THE COYNE HOUSE, MOUNT FOREST.

SECURING breakfast the party departed in the ox-wagons for Mount Forest, 14 miles away, over a very bad road. The Garafraxa at that period was a miserable highway. On high land the footing was solid enough, but on low land and swampy soil, where water would accumulate, the wagon wheels cut deeply into the soil and rendered progress extremely slow; while over the pure swamps where causewaying had been laid down, the bumping of wheels from log to log—and there were oftentimes long stretches of these—made the word " corduroy " one long to be remembered by the pioneers.

From Arthur, the Garafraxa led due north-west, angling across Arthur Township. Many large streams were crossed in this traverse—branches of the Conestogo running south-west and south to empty into the Grand River in Waterloo Township and County, the Grand itself emptying into Lake Erie at Port Maitland.

Other streams ran west and north-west, being branches of the Maitland emptying into Lake Huron at Menesetung (Goderich), or the Saugeen, emptying into the same body of water at the mouth or Southampton.

In fact, Arthur Township, with the neighbouring ones of Proton, Luther and Melanchthon, are the highest points in north-western Ontario, and form the watershed to streams running to the north, north-west, west and south, to empty finally into such widely separated bodies of water as the Georgian Bay, Lakes Huron and Erie.

DEER AND WOLVES.

Adjacent to the road were occasional clearings, with here and there a settler's shanty; except for these, all else was dense, primeval forest—the home of wild Indians and wild beasts.

The day was dark and lowering, with occasional showers of rain. A cold wind blew from the north. A

halt was made at noon by a small stream for the midday meal. The oxen were outspanned and given hay
and grain and an hour's rest.

Shortly after inspanning and resuming the march, a
crashing noise in the woods on the right broke on the
ears of the travellers, followed by the howls of a pack
of wolves, and immediately thereafter a doe burst out
on to the clearing ahead of the leading ox-team and
dashed away down the roadway, followed by half a
dozen grey wolves.

The doe had been wounded and was almost spent.
The grey beasts quickly gained upon her. One, the
leader of the pack—a large he-wolf—raced alongside the
panting deer, and with a mighty bound fastened his
teeth in her throat. The remainder of the pack quickly
fastened upon the doe's haunches, and deer and wolves
fell to the roadway in a struggling mass. Quickly all
was over.

The Beaumonts had not been idle during this passage.
Quickly grasping their muskets, Guy and Alex raced
after the flying deer, and coming within rifle-shot of the
struggling mass, delivered a few shots at the grey
marauders. One fell dead, and another, limping off,
was joined by the others, who scattered into the surrounding forest.

Running up to the wounded doe, they found her still
alive but dying, her life-blood pulsing away from the
torn throat where the teeth of the he-wolf had torn the
jugulars. She turned her large gazelle-like eyes upon
the boys as if seeking pity, but these were quickly
glazed over in death.

Upon the wagons arriving, the oxen refused to pass
by the dead deer because of the smell of blood. The

deer was therefore dragged to one side by the men and portions cut off to serve as food on their journey.

"The poor deer!" exclaimed Mrs. Beaumont. "What awful beasts those wolves are! I declare, John, I'm afraid they will attack us on the road. How much farther is it to Mount Forest? Oh, if I have to pass the night on this road!" and the pioneer's wife shuddered and covered her face with her hands.

"Don't worry, mother. We will be in Mount Forest by night. It can't be more than 6 or 8 miles away. Don't fear. The wolves will not attack us."

"But they may attack the oxen, and what will become of us then?" said his wife. "Oh! why did we ever leave dear Woolwich to come into this awful bush'!" and the terror-stricken woman covered her face and cried.

"Now, now, mother! This is all nonsense!" cried Beaumont. "There's not a particle of danger of the wolves attacking either us or the oxen. There are three of us here and well armed, and if a wolf shows himself he will quickly get his medicine. However, Guy, you and Alex take your muskets and tramp on ahead; Jack can guide the second ox-team."

Accordingly, Guy and Alex trudged on ahead to ward off any hidden danger, with Guy considerably in the lead. After traversing about a mile, Guy arrived at a large stream crossing the roadway at right angles and running westwards. It was the south or main branch of the Saugeen River. Here a rough bridge of hewn logs laid upon timbers crossed the stream.

At this point the forest on both sides of the roadway approached the sides of the travelled highway, and a short bend in the latter prevented Guy, who was some distance in advance of Alex, seeing the bridge until he was almost upon it. What was his consternation, on opening the bridge, to behold the figure of a blanketed Indian, with gun in hand, upon the farther end of the bridge and in the act of turning to come towards him.

Guy's first impulse was to jump back and plunge into the surrounding forest, but the Indian had already turned and seen him. The Indian was tall, with high cheek-bones, dark eyes, a high-bridged nose, raven black hair made into a pleat and hanging down his back, and with a solitary eagle feather fastened to his hair and flowing backwards over one ear.

He had on leather leggings and moccasins, and had his body and shoulders covered with a blanket fastened together at his breast. In the crook of his left arm he carried a cocked gun, and, with the finger of his right hand upon the trigger, he was truly an alarming figure to burst unexpectedly upon one in the dense forest. However, it appeared later he was shooting muskrats, which at this time of year were plentiful in the river. The Indian had made the bridge a beat or sentry-go to watch the stream up and down for his game. He already had a pile of ten or a dozen rats at one end of the bridge.

"Bosho, nitchi! (Good day, friend)," cried Guy, anxious to be on good footing, in view of the gun, with the aborigine.

"Bosho! Bosho!" replied the Indian. "White man got Ishketawabo (whisky)?" Guy shook his head; he did not understand. "White man got fire-water?" again inquired the Indian. "Indian give beaver-skin for bottle fire-water."

"No, we have no fire-water," replied Guy. "My father and mother are coming down the road, and they will tell you we have no fire-water." At this instant a very unwelcome visitor appeared upon the scene. As before mentioned, the river crossed the roadway at right angles, running from right to left. For perhaps 50 yards to the eastwards the stream was in sight, but there a bend to the southward, with the dense forest coming to the water's edge, hid it from sight.

Around this bend now floated a large log, about 20 feet in length, in lumber jack parlance, an old "homestead," and seated upon the middle of it upon his haunches sat a large black bear. The river being high, due to the spring rains and full from bank to bank and the current running swiftly, the log rapidly approached the bridge.

At first sight of the beast the Indian levelled his gun and fired point-blank at the bear, but as the weapon was loaded only with duck shot, the only effect thus produced was to anger the bear.

Guy now took hasty aim with his musket and fired. The ball struck the bear in the shoulder and served to still further infuriate the animal, and as the log approached the bridge, which was only a few feet above the swollen waters, he sprang on to the structure and made for the hunters, who were rapidly reloading their weapons. Their position was now one of extreme peril.

The Indian, who was nearest the maddened animal, sprang upon the parapet of the bridge and ran rapidly along its length, with the bear in swift pursuit below him. In the act of springing up to seize the Indian, the bear suddenly found himself enveloped in the folds of the blanket, which the Indian had hastily unloosed from his shoulders and deftly cast over the head of the enraged animal.

The few seconds it took the bear to tear off the

blanket, which he did with snarls and deep growls, tearing it into shreds, gave the Indian time to jump off the parapet and rush to the nearest tree on the roadway, and up which he rapidly shinned, but his feet barely

INDIAN OUTWITS BEAR.

escaped the opened jaws of the bear, which had quickly pursued him.

Guy in the meantime had run back a few yards, and, selecting a tree, rapidly mounted upwards, taking his musket along with him. Astride one of its lower branches, he carefully reloaded his musket, and taking careful aim at the bear, who was now endeavouring to climb the Indian's tree, planted a ball behind the animal's foreleg, which brought him heavily to the ground, where he lay thrashing about amongst the leaves.

On hearing the shots John Beaumont and Alex had rapidly run forward, guns in hand, ahead of the ox-teams, and approached the bridge, and seeing the bear planted another shot into the beast's breast between the forelegs. The animal then stiffened and lay still.

" Hello, dad ! We've had an exciting time, but I think my last shot fixed Mr. Bruin !" cried Guy.

" How did it happen?" asked the father. Guy rapidly recounted the affair. " It is very odd a bear should be riding a log down the river," said the father. " Most probably it was in some jamb higher up the river, and the bear wishing to cross, his weight dis-lodged the timber on which he was crossing, and so he floated down here."

The Indian and Guy now descended from their trees and the teams coming up, the incident was retold to Mrs. Beaumont and the girls.

" Bears and wolves and wild beasts of men fighting and killing ! What a dreadful land ! John Beaumont, you are taking me and my children into these wild woods where we will all be killed !" exclaimed his wife.

" Now, now, mother ! Don't start that again. Don't be alarmed. Nobody is hurt. You must remember we are in the ' Bush ' where wild animals are in plenty. We will soon be in Mount Forest," replied her husband.

On inquiring from the Indian how far the latter was

distant, the Indian held up two fingers and said: "Wigwams two hours' walk over there," pointing with his hand to the northward.

The bridge was crossed by the teams, and as the afternoon was waning fast, the ox-teams were urged to their best pace in order to reach the settlement before night had fallen. This part of the Garafraxa had more solid bottom than that to the south of the river. There were fewer swamps to traverse, and therefore fewer causeways to cross, but night had already fallen, and full two hours had passed before the leading ox-team, ascending slightly higher ground, entered a clearing in which lights shining from a few scattered houses told them that they had reached Mount Forest and the end of their day's journey.

Passing rapidly up the main street, they came at length to a large two-storey frame building from which lights gleamed from several windows—the old Coyne House, run by Isaac Coyne. Here they secured quarters for the night, and after stabling the cattle and securing some supper, all retired to rest, worn out with the toil and excitement of the day.

CHAPTER X.

HUNTER'S HOTEL, DURHAM.

SHORTLY after leaving Mount Forest the road brought the party into the County of Grey. From this point, as before mentioned, the Garafraxa ceased angling and ran almost due north for 40 or 50 miles, to strike the Georgian Bay at Sydenham (or Owen Sound).

After passing over 5 miles north of Mount Forest the road entered the Long Swamp. This swamp was on the boundary between Normanby and Egremont Townships, and was the "bête-noire" of all the early settlers whose way led over it. It was about a mile in length, and its depth, in some places, unknown. A corduroy causeway had been laid across it, but in many places this had sunk almost out of sight, being covered with water, but piles of brush in successive layers, cut from the surrounding swamps, had been piled upon it to make it passable.

This operation had to be frequently repeated, as the road—due to the traffic—kept sinking. At times the struggling oxen could scarce drag the wagon through the accumulated mass of logs, brush and water of the road, and to leave the middle of the highway was to sink wagon and animals out of sight in the swamp.

Our party had not entered the swamp more than a quarter of a mile, when they came upon a wagon load of settlers in distress. These proved to be Philip Neubecker and family—old neighbours from Woolwich

Township, also trekking to the Saugeen country. The family consisted of the father and mother, Stephen, the eldest son, a young man of 20 years, Frank, his younger brother, and two girls—Katie and Lena—these latter of 16 and 18 years of age respectively. The family had put up overnight at the Queen's Hotel, Mount Forest, and so did not know of the presence there of the Beaumont family. They had left Mount Forest early that morning, but in a particularly bad spot in the swamp had broken the front axle of their wagon, and were, when overtaken by the Beaumonts, in a dilemma what to do.

"I'll tell you what you can do, Philip," said John Beaumont. "We will cut brush enough to fill in one side of the roadway and allow our ox-teams to pass you, then unhitch your oxen, and we will unload and turn your wagon about when, by arranging a sapling under your broken axle to act as a 'runner,' you and the boys can have it drawn back to Mount Forest and repaired. Mrs. Neubecker and the girls can come along in our wagons and await your coming at Hunter's Hotel in Bentinck."

This was agreed to as being the best way of handling the matter, and presently, when sufficient brush had been cut and laid down, the Beaumont teams succeeded in passing the broken-down wagon. Neubecker's goods were unloaded and the wagon turned about, and an artificial wheel in the shape of a peeled sapling placed under the broken axle.

During this time Stephen Neubecker had gone over to the Beaumont wagons and had warmly shaken hands with Mrs. Beaumont and the girls.

"So you are going to the Saugeen country, too, Stephen?" cried Alice Beaumont.

"Yes. I had to follow you, Alice, you know," replied Stephen, with a smile. The girl reddened but made no comment. "Yes," continued Stephen "somewheres up there dad intends to locate. I hope it will be near you folks," and he looked with an admiring glance at Alice.

"Oh, won't that be fine! It will be just like old times back in Woolwich!" exclaimed Alice.

"Have you had a pleasant trip?" asked Stephen.

"Oh, awful! Dreadful!" exclaimed Mrs. Beaumont. "Wild beasts and wild men! All the way! I hope you folks, Stephen, keep near us for protection. I'm sure we'll need it."

"Oh, there is little real danger," replied Stephen. "One must get accustomed to the 'Bush' and its ways."

"Well, I don't know. What I've seen of the 'Bush' is awful. Those dreadful men at Arthur and those awful grey wolves and the poor deer! I shudder when I think of it!" cried Mrs. Beaumont.

"Won't you stay with us, Stephen?" cried Alice. "I'm sure you will. The others can go back to Mount Forest."

"I think so," said Steve. "There is no necessity for me to return to Mount Forest. Dad and Frank with the oxen can easily get the wagon back to the settlement and repaired, while we can push on to Hunter's."

It was finally so arranged, and Stephen took his place at the head of the second ox-team, relieving Alex. This arrangement was very pleasing to Stephen, as it placed him near Miss Alice, with whom he exchanged frequent repartees to while away the tedium of the journey.

Pushing on, the party finally crossed the long swamp

and struck more solid ground. A few miles further along they crossed another tributary stream to the Saugeen—the Beatty, flowing to the westwards—and reached more hilly country, and finally towards evening on travelling up a long hill reached Hunter's Hotel, Bentinck.

Here a large two-storey hotel, together with some scattered buildings, formed the town. It was a central point for the settlers from the surrounding country, because of the fact that here resided the Crown Lands Agent, George Jackson, for the location and sale of of lands in Grey and Bruce.

On inquiring for quarters for the night, Mr. Hunter, the proprietor, said : " We are pretty full. My wife has had a quilting bee to-day, and there are some 30 or 40 women here. Mostly settlers' wives and daughters. Some of them will soon be leaving for their homes, but many will remain over the night. However, we can give you a ' shake-down ' somewhere, if that will suit you ?"

" Oh, perfectly !" said Beaumont. " We are accustomed to roughing it."

" So !" returned the tavern keeper. " Well, make yourselves at home. Supper will soon be ready." The party then entered the hotel, where Mrs. Hunter took charge of the women folks—took them to her own room, where they took off wraps and had a refreshing wash after their long journey.

Mrs. Hunter was a very kindly disposed, friendly and motherly woman, and as the incidents of the trip were recounted to her held up her hands in dismay, exclaiming to Mrs. Beaumont : " Oh, my dear, we have no such wild beasts up here ! At least, I've not seen any.

And as for fighting, Jim will not allow anything of the kind in the house."

"Yes, but you've dense forest here, and where forest is there are wild animals," spoke up Alice with a merry glance in her eyes, "and also where whisky is, there men will fight," she added.

"Not here!" persisted Mrs. Hunter. "But don't let's talk about it. Come along and see my beautiful quilts."

Conducting them to a large adjoining room, where some 35 to 40 women sat around quilting frames, busily engaged on the different patterns, she introduced Mrs. Beaumont and girls to the quilters, and then began an inspection of the quilts. Each quilt had a different design. The patterns had been marked out with coloured chalk. The core of the quilt was composed of cotton-wool, between two sheets of factory cotton or ordinary print goods. Upon these the patterns had been traced in chalk, which the quilters followed in their sewing. There were six quilting frames, supported at the corners of the backs of four chairs, and each frame was surrounded by from six to eight women busily sewing.

The first quilt was a log cabin pattern in different colours, of which the shades ran across the goods in bands of colour. Another quilt had the pattern of a star, while others had "T" and "S" patterns. A fifth frame held a fan pattern, while the sixth and last was a so-called "beggarman's quilt"; that is, no pattern at all, the quilt being sewn higgledy-piggledy.

Mrs. Beaumont and the girls praised the quilts and the skill of the quilters, and the supper bell ringing just then, they all adjourned to the dining room for the evening meal.

After supper the young men from the surrounding homesteads began pouring into the hotel, and presently the sound of violins tuning up was heard, and a bunch of young people pressed forwards and declared they wanted the dining room for a dance.

Mrs. Hunter kindly consented and the place was quickly cleared of furniture, and in a very short time the room was filled with the flying forms of the young people of the settlement engaged in the mazes of the dance.

Quadrilles, schottisches, a dance in two-four time; polkas, a round dance three steps to a measure; mazurkas, a slow polka, waltz and reels followed in quick succession until an intermission was called about 11 o'clock, and Mrs. Hunter had a dainty lunch passed around to the dancers.

After lunch a call was made for a " Cutting-out jig," and, coupled with the request, the names of a Miss Kitty Walsh and a Mr. Jack Purdy. The request was greeted with applause by the crowd. This dance was performed by two people—a man and a woman—each dancing until exhausted, when a member of the same sex stepped in to release the dancer.

The two persons who were now called to the floor by the crowd were a Miss Kitty Walsh, daughter of a near-by settler, and a Mr. Jack Purdy, a neighbouring farmer.

The musicians struck up " Money Musk," and Jack and Kitty took the floor. Both were accomplished step dancers. It was square heel and toe dancing. Jack, with his hands resting lightly on his hips, rattled the floor with a noise like castanets as he circled around Miss Kitty, while that young lady, no whit behind her partner in activity and skill, with her gown grasped on either side and slightly raised to allow free action of her little feet, returned tap for tap to the run of the tune as they circled around each other to the vociferous plaudits of the many onlookers. Suddenly the musicians varied the tune to " McIntyre's Jig," then

CUTTING-OUT JIG.

to " Carney's Fancy," followed by " Donnybrook Fair," and finally to " Larry Reilly," but to all of these the dancers kept perfect time. This was kept up for some time, until finally Jack gave unmistakable signs of exhaustion, when another young man named Tom Dickson jumped in to take his place, leaving Miss

Kitty victorious. Her place was then taken by another young lady, and the dance went on.

Midnight had long passed ere the party broke up, and the pioneers returned to rest with the feeling of having spent a most enjoyable evening.

Next morning young Jack Beaumont was ill, complained of headache and chills, and kind Mrs. Hunter packed him off to bed and plied him with frequent hot drinks, so that by evening he was blooming red with an attack of measles.

This caused an alteration in the father's plans; plainly they could not go on into the "Bush" and leave Jack behind. The Neubeckers also had to await the arrival of their wagon and household goods from Mount Forest.

In this predicament John Beaumont decided to take a few days off on a land hunting expedition into the adjoining townships of Egremont and Glenelg, lying to the east and south-east.

Securing supplies, therefore, from Mrs. Hunter, and accompanied by his sons Guy and Stephen Neubecker, on the second night of his arrival in Bentinck, the trio struck off into the township lying north-east of the of the settlement, and taking along their guns for use in case of game.

The first forenoon they found the country more hilly and of a lighter soil than that over which they had passed from Mount Forest. Also there were many stones, but still everything was covered with good hard wood timber. During that first forenoon their passage over the "blazed" trail was slow; by noon they camped by the side of a small spring stream several miles east of Hunter's and prepared their midday meal.

While engaged in this business a whining noise

above their heads caused them to look up, to discover a large eagle flash downwards with a lightning dash into the stream beside them, from which he immediately arose bearing a long weasel-shaped black body and with a long bushy tail—a mink—in his talons.

The eagle soared majestically upwards in circles of perhaps 100 yards in diameter. Rapidly he mounted upwards higher and higher into the blue empyrean, until both eagle and victim became a small black ball in the blue vault of the sky. Suddenly the black ball appeared to become stationary, interrupted presently by a flutter and a side-slip motion downwards by the bird of prey. Another pause and another side-slip, until presently it was seen the mink had squirmed upwards on the eagle's leg and had sunk his teeth into the fleshy part of the thigh of the bird of prey, from which the blood was now running in a stream.

The eagle circled lower and lower, becoming weaker and weaker from the loss of blood, until, finally, bird and mink from a height of probably 70 feet fell with a crash upon the sward close to the hunting party.

The mink now endeavoured to disengage himself from the strong, sharp talons of the Monarch of the Air, whose claws appeared to pierce the hide of the animal.

The party now approached the pair and found a large Golden Eagle of about 8-ft. spread of wings, with a strong hooked beak, bright flashing eyes and powerful claws. The blood continued flowing from the leg wounds, and presently the eagle's eyes glazed in death.

While Guy held a crotched stick against the mink's neck, pinning him to the ground, Steve released the eagle's talons, and on Guy moving the crotched stick, the animal sprang away and was quickly lost in the undergrowth.

"You should have held him, Guy," said Stephen.

"No. He deserved his liberty," said Guy; "besides, the pelt is worthless at this time of year."

The party now struck northwards through the centre of the township, coming finally to a large river—the Rocky Saugeen—one of the main tributaries to the Saugeen proper, and the party followed along its banks eastwards, but by evening John Beaumont had decided the land in Glenelg was not suitable to his taste—in his estimation being too hilly, too stony and too rough. Coming to this decision, the party camped for the night and decided the next day to explore the township to the south, viz., Egremont.

A camp fire was built, two crotched sticks about 4 ft. long were driven into the ground and about 8 ft. apart. Upon these a thick limb was placed, and from this crosslimb branches and bushes were laid sloping downwards to the ground, forming an enclosure, with the three sides closed in and with the fourth open and facing the fire.

The ground underneath was covered with hemlock boughs for a bed, and here, after supper, the tired land hunters found shelter and warmth for the night. From time to time one or other member of the party arose and replenished the fire.

Early on the next morning after breakfast the camp was struck, and the party made off to the southward. After travelling about four miles another large branch of the Saugeen was reached, and was that flowing westwards through Hunter's in Bentinck. This proved not to be so wide nor deep as the rocky branch further to the north. Travelling up its banks, they came to where a huge elm tree had fallen across the stream. Guy and his father passed dry shod over this, but Stephen by some mischance slipped and was precipitated into the stream. Although the water was deep and with considerable current, Stephen was a good swimmer and made the shore, and presently climbed out on the southern shore, with his clothes plastered to his body. This accident compelled a halt in the land seeking until afternoon. A fire was built, and Stephen disrobed and hung his sodden clothes around the camp fire to dry.

By mid-afternoon this was accomplished, and the party then resumed their tramp to the southwards. After passing over another 4 or 4½ miles, they struck the Surveyor's "blaze" running east and west and marking the boundary between Glenelg and Egremont.

After tramping several miles to the southward they found the character of the country changing. From hills and gravel they found a more level country—in fact, too level—as they found frequent swamps, and because of the level land considerable standing water.

In this way three days more passed hunting, camping and land seeking. At night the cries of wolf packs were frequently heard in pursuit of deer, but none were seen.

At length John Beaumont finally came to the conclusion there was too much level land and standing water, that because of this seeding would always be late when the country was turned into farming land, so that on the morning of the fourth day they decided to return to Hunter's in Bentinck and resume their original quest of homes in the Saugeen country to the westwards.

On their homeward journey that day Guy, who was in advance, saw a small black animal resembling a small dog with a bushy tail run along the "blaze" ahead of him. It did not run very fast, and Guy sprang forward to head the animal off. Immediately the animal stopped, rolled itself into a ball, and, as Guy approached it, he became conscious of sharp pains in his shins and legs. On looking down he found his clothing perforated with short quills, some of which had gone through the cloth and pierced the flesh. On stooping to withdraw them the animal made off into the woods, and his father coming up asked what was the matter. On Guy showing him the quills, he remarked :

" Why, that was a porcupine. You should not have gone near him. Pull all of the quills out of the flesh and bathe the limbs in the nearest creek. You will have a pair of sore legs for a couple of weeks from those quills."

This Guy did, and found his limbs had become quite sore, so much so that by nightfall, when they had again reached Hunter's, the skin was swollen and inflamed, but kind Mrs. Hunter applied wild hop poultices to them, so that by morning Guy was able to resume the original journey. They also found Jack so much better of his attack of measles as to be able to be up and be about, only troubled now and again by a hacking cough.

The party then decided they would start for Brant the next morning. Philip Neubecker and Frank had meanwhile arrived two days before from Mount Forest with his repaired ox-wagon, and taking aboard his wife and daughters, struck out for Buck's Crossing, leaving word with Mrs. Beaumont for his son Stephen to follow him.

CHAPTER XI.

BUCK'S CROSSING.

ABRAHAM BUCK was a man of middle life when he decided to enter the "Queen's Bush" in search of a home. In company with Thomas Jasper the two men arrived at Bentinck (now Durham) in May, 1849.

On interviewing George Jackson, Crown Lands Agent at Bentinck, at that time and for many years afterwards, and on stating their wish to take up "Bush" farms, they were told to select whatever lands they wished, as only three other settlers—Lamont, Weir and Brown— had gone in before them.

Accordingly, they struck westwards through Bentinck Township, and after some days exploring selected lands on each side of the County Line between Bruce and Grey, Thomas Jasper settling a short distance to the west of the County Line and in Brant Township, and Abraham Buck a short distance east of the County Line and in Bentinck Township and Grey County.

At the eastern end of the present town of Hanover, and perhaps 100 yards south of the site of the present (1922) Truax factory and on the north side of the Durham Road, Buck erected his log cabin, being the first building erected in Bentinck Township and in the south-western part of the County of Grey.

The surrounding country was fairly level and covered with heavy timber. Due north about half a mile ran the Saugeen River, and at that spot, owing to a bend in the stream, a jamb of logs had formed and served as a bridge to the northern shore, hence the name " Buck's Crossing."

Abraham Buck had two sons, William and George, and several daughters. The sons were big boys in their late teens at the time their father entered the " Bush." Being big and strong, they materially helped in the process of building a home and clearing the land.

Buck's first effort was directed to securing a shelter, and barely was his house erected when an inflow of settlers began. As it was the only house for many miles on that part of the Durham Road it was a frequent place of call. Settlers, both on going into the " Bush " to seek land and returning to Durham to register their location at the Land Office, always stopped at " Buck's."

Abraham Buck and his sons gradually increased the area of their clearing, chopping and logging, sowing and planting. They were friendly in the extreme to the strings of new settlers pouring into the new lands to the west and north. Their latch string always hung out to the weary traveller, who was always sure of a kindly reception, a bed and food at Abraham Buck's home.

The Buck family has long since been scattered—some of the younger members to the prairies of the west—but Abraham Buck himself and his kind-hearted wife have long slept the sleep that knows no waking; but the memory of the many kindnesses received at their hands by many an old settler of the Saugeen Country still lives and blooms in the hearts of those who settled in the early days in " The Queen's Bush."

CHAPTER XII.

FLOATING DOWN THE SAUGEEN.

NEAR Buck's Crossing and a short distance to the westward, the two main streams of the Saugeen—the north and the south branches, the latter of which our pioneers had already passed miles away and days before south of Mount Forest, when the bear attacked the Indian —united to form a large and deep river with a moderate current, flowing westwards and north-westwards through almost the whole length of the County of Bruce, to finally empty into Lake Huron at the mouth.

As already mentioned, to the north of Buck's Cabin and in the dense woods a huge jam had formed at a bend in the river. This jam was composed of logs, trees and stumps brought down in huge numbers by the spring rise, and formed a solid roadway of timber extending from shore to shore and up stream for a quarter of a mile.

For some considerable time, until a bridge was later built across the Saugeen to the west of Buck's Cabin, this jam formed the only means the early settlers had of crossing the river at this point to get into the northern part of Bentinck Township, the adjacent Townships of Brant and Elderslie, or of those still further back.

John Beaumont was anxious to go farther west. As there was no roadway from the crossing farther west, Abraham Buck strongly advised him to build a raft and to place his family and goods upon it and float down the river twelve or fifteen miles—as some other settlers had already done that spring—to the western part of Brant Township, where was heavy timber and presumably good soil to be found. This Beaumont accordingly did.

In a few days he and the boys, with the occasional help of Mr. Buck and his sons, built a stout raft 14 feet wide by 30 feet long. The raft was built of cedar

FLOATING DOWN THE SAUGEEN.

logs, pinned together by wooden bolts secured to cross pieces of timber, and formed a fairly roomy structure. Upon this was deposited the wagons with the wheels removed; the household goods, farm implements and the oxen—these latter secured to uprights an improvised stable. At one end of the raft a cookhouse was built and a stove set up.

Therefore, on the morning of the fifth day after reaching Buck's Crossing, the party was ready for the

Saugeen, and bidding adieu to the hospitable Buck family, entrusted their fortunes to the river.

The current of the Saugeen was gentle and moderate. Its width varied from 75 to 100 yards; its depth also varied, in some places very deep, and in others only a couple of feet. In the early days of settlement, due largely to the great area of forest, the streams held much more water than at present. The clearing of the land, the removal of logs and brush causing jams in the waterway, and the ditching and draining of the tilled soil, all combined to furnish a more rapid exit of the waters due to spring thaws and the melting of the winter's snows.

The river wound its way westwards; at times between high banks densely covered with primeval forest; at times opening out forest glades where wild deer were seen browsing. Flocks of wild duck were frequently seen on rounding some bend in the river, busily engaged in fishing for minnows. The mighty pine, the towering elm, the wide-spreading beech, but above all the broad-leaved sugar maple—in dense masses—covered either shore.

Towards noon—on rounding a bend in the river—the pioneers discovered an open glade, with a troop of wild deer gazing at a combat between two bucks. These monarchs of the forest were evidently disputing the championship of herd. One, the heavier and older, with antlers of seven tine, backed away from the other and younger but more active opponent. As they rushed together in mortal combat, the crash of their antlered heads resounded through the forest aisles, the older and heavier of the two animals bearing back the younger and lighter. But the latter by a sudden spring bounded to one side, and with a lightning movement of the head ripped a slash along the side of the older animal. Instantly a red gash showed and the red blood poured out.

Breaking away, the animals again came together with a terrorizing crash, whose echoes resounded down the river. Both animals went down, but only one—the younger—arose. The older remained still, its neck

COMBAT OF THE BUCKS.

broken. The conqueror walked around his antagonist, snorting and stamping. At length, evidently realizing its rival was dead, drew off and joined the herd of does, whose attention being now drawn to the figures on the raft, turned and bounded off into the forest.

At noon the raft drew into the bank and anchored for dinner. Following down the river bank for some distance, Guy shot some wild ducks, while Alex and Jack trekked back up-stream to where the fallen buck lay,

and stripping off the hide, secured some venison steak
which would furnish a savoury stew for their repast.

Casting off again in the early afternoon, they floated
gently onwards, new scenes opening out on either bank
—glades covered with wild flowers, violets, dandelions
and wild roses, succeeded by thickets of wild plum and
cherry trees, whose foliage was one mass of white
bloom, and whose blossoms made the air redolent with
their perfume.

BEAR AND RAFT.

About mid-afternooon, on entering a wide stretch of
the river, they discerned a black object in the water a
short distance from the left or southern shore, and
which appeared to be moving across the stream. On
nearer approach, they discovered it to be a black bear
swimming to the northern bank. The oxen now
became restless and gave signs of leaping off the raft,
and it took the combined efforts of Beaumont and his
sons to prevent their doing so. Meantime the raft had

borne down upon the bear, who, placing his fore-paws upon the front logs, quickly clambered aboard the floating structure.

All was now confusion and terror upon the raft. The snorting oxen tore loose the halters which held them and sprang overboard and swam towards the southern shore, while the screaming of the women added pandemonium to the exciting scene.

There was no time to secure the guns, so hastily snatching up his guiding pole, John Beaumont brought it down swiftly upon Bruin's head, knocking him overboard, where Guy, who also had grabbed up a guiding pole, began poking at the beast. The bear again endeavoured to clamber on board, but John Beaumont's pole brought sharply upon his paws prevented him.

Guy then secured one of the muskets and planted a ball into the bear's head, which caused him to thrash about in the water, while the current bore the raft onwards. "We must kill him or he will attack the oxen on the shore!" shouted Beaumont, and securing his own musket planted several shots into the animal's neck and shoulders, upon which the beast quickly sank in the river. This exciting episode concluded, the Beaumonts headed the raft for the southern shore—where the cattle had landed—and moored it securely to the bank. The father and sons then began scouring the adjacent forest for the terror-stricken oxen. After a long hunt these were found quietly browsing at some low bushes. They were finally secured, and after some trouble again gotten on board the raft; the latter again cast off from the shore and the river journey was again resumed.

By evening they had reached some high clay banks on the northern shore. It was a lovely scene. The river valley at this point widened out to the southward, and extended from the water's edge for a space of perhaps a thousand acres. The western side of this southern valley rose gently into hills which, aproaching, formed again the western and south-western banks of the river. Back of this open valley the unbroken forest stretched away to the south and west. The valley itself was covered with thickets of wild red plum trees now in their whitest bloom. The rays of the setting sun lit up the entrancing scene. It is said of two of the early explorers of this region—Auld Scotia's sons, standing on the high northern bank of the river and looking out over this inspiring scene—that one remarked: "Eh, mon! if Paradise was anything like yon, Adam was a 'fule' to eat the apple!"

At the western end of the valley the river turned again to the north-west, and wound its way and was lost between the dark walls of the forest. After viewing the scene for some time the pioneers decided to tie up there for the night. The craft was firmly moored to the southern bank and preparations made to pass the night. Fires were made on shore and shelters or lean-tos built. During this time huge flocks of wild pigeons passed overhead, flying in a north-west direction—the flocks being so great as to darken the setting sun and with a sound as of waves breaking on a rocky shore.

The night passed uneventfully. By daybreak everybody was up and preparing for the day's work. Fires were made and breakfast prepared, the oxen fed, and the raft cast off from the shore. As they floated onwards dense forests still covered either shore. Deer were occasionally observed swimming across the stream, while wild ducks flew overhead.

At noon they again moored the raft to the bank as they had the day before and prepared dinner. Casting off again they resumed their river road, and by mid-afternoon they reached a glade on the northern shore not far from where the present Deer Creek empties into the Saugeen. Here a beautiful glade of several acres in extent, surrounded by the dense forest, met their gaze.

A landing was made, and whilst preparations for a meal went forward, John Beaumont shouldered his gun and, with an axe, made off into the surrounding forest prospecting. Heavy hardwood timber stretched away to the north and east. The soil appeared good. After scouting around for several miles and marking the trees with a "blaze" for his return, he again returned to camp, discovering on his approach to the clearing a spring stream of good water.

Reaching camp, he announced his decision that they would make their future home there. Temporary shelters of lean-tos were at once erected and preparations began for erecting a shanty on the following day. That night speculations and anticipations were discussed by the members of Beaumont's family as to the prospects of their future home there.

The first night in camp a tremendous noise of flapping wings and breaking branches woke up the settlers. The following morning an investigation revealed a "pigeon roost" in the neighbouring forest. It appeared thousands of pigeons used it nightly as a "roost." The earth below the trees was covered with droppings and eggs. Many branches had broken off from the weight of the birds sitting upon them. A number were shot to supply the larder. Thereafter the pioneers never lacked for pigeon pie or pigeon stew.

During the next day a rough shanty of logs covered with elm bark was put up to serve until a proper house could be built, which John Beaumont said would be his first care.

During the evening of the second day a party of Indians arrived at the clearing in canoes and made a camp on the edge of the glade. They had come up the river from the mouth and were on a hunting and trapping expedition. They comprised six bucks and their squaws.

That evening Guy strolled down to their camp and found they were Chippewas from down river. They were friendly and able to speak broken English.

" Bosho ! " said Guy.

" Bosho ! Nitchi ! " replied a tall, finely-formed Indian. " White man build house. Will live here ? "

" Yes," said Guy, " this is to be our home, and we will take up land here."

The Indian looked darkly at this.

" Plenty fish. Plenty pigeon. Much deer. White man come and drive them all away," he replied.

" No, no," said Guy. " We are going to clear the land and grow grain and live by farming. We will not make war upon the wild game. That is for our Indian brothers. Of course, now and then we will kill a deer for meat when we have no other."

This seemed to mollify the spokesman of the party and he became more friendly, and pointing his finger at Guy, said :

" You name ? "

" Guy Beaumont, and my father is John Beaumont," said Guy.

The Indian nodded, and said :

" Me John Kubassey, and him "—pointing to a thick-set Indian standing by his side—" Peter Niwash."

Guy bowed to the introduction, and said : " I'm

6

pleased to meet you. I hope we will always be good friends and neighbours; if not, I'm sure it will not be our fault."

"Good!" said Kubassey. "All this," extending his arm and sweeping it around towards forest and river, "was made by the Great Spirit for his Red and White children."

Guy bowed assent to this statement, and then, shaking hands with the two Indians—who appeared to be the leaders of the party—returned to his camp, where he related to his father what had occurred.

Next morning Peter Niwash came to the house with a string of fish—beautiful trout with speckled sides— reflecting the colours of the rainbow. In return, Mrs. Beaumont presented the Indian with a batch of scones hot from the oven, which caused the Indian's face to light up. "Good squaw! Good heart! Indian no forget!" and returned to the camp.

The Sauking Band—of which these Indians formed a part, later corrupted into Saugeen—were a tribe of the ancient Objibway Nation (Chippewa) who had originally inhabited the northern shores of Lake Superior, both shores of Lake Michigan, and the peninsula of old Upper Canada, down as far as Detroit, since shortly after Champlain's time.

In many bloody battles this nation had conquered the fierce Iroquois—those human tigers of the Canadian Forest—of whom the Senecas, the Onondagos and Oneidas were the fiercest, the Mohawks, the Cayugas and the Tuscaroras being less so. These six Nations had destroyed the Hurons of Champlain's time about the year 1649, and their hunting grounds were the region we have been describing, and which extended from the region around the present Parry Sound, south and westwards to the Erie and Huron Seas.

It is a sad reflection to think, and speaks ill for the Indian character, that of all the centuries they had occupied the American Continent, even from that October day in 1492 when they had first come in contact with the white man in the person of Columbus, down to the present time, they had never gotten beyond the arts of hunting and fishing. Inventive genius they had none. Their wild and untamed nature was evidenced in the wretched hovels in which they dwelt, their cruel tortures of enemy prisoners, and their tribal orgies.

At the edge of Beaumont's clearing and close to the encircling forest, as mentioned, a spring of clear water gushed forth, its outflow forming a small stream which ran through the clearing and emptied into the river. This spring furnished the house with water. One evening Alice Beaumont, now dawning into womanhood, went to the spring for water. As she stooped to fill her pail a slight noise in the forest close at hand caused her to raise her head, when two glowing eyeballs and the body of a beast stretched along a limb some ten feet above her head struck paralysis through her frame.

Her terror was so great she sank backwards upon the ground in a faint. As she did so the beast, with a low snarl, sprang at the sinking form. But scarce had the animal left the limb and was yet in mid-air when a rifle-shot rang out, the beast turned over and over, and sank dead beside the fainting girl.

A dark form rushed up, and proved to be Peter Niwash, the Indian, who, returning from a deer hunt, had crossed the clearing on his way to his camp behind Alice and noted the danger. As Alice recovered from her faint he assisted her to her feet, and then turned the dead animal over and discovered it to be a cata-mount, or lynx.

The following month more settlers began coming in, mostly by river, which was now the " Bush " high-way. The Neubeckers had already located further to the west. The Stewarts, Browns, Smiths, Jaspers, Boultons, Godfreys, Everetts and Haags—the latter old acquaintances from Woolwich Township—these all settled further down river or to the west, the Neubeckers being the nearest neighbours on the eastern side of the river. They were of German stock, and as before mentioned, came from Woolwich Township, Waterloo County, and consisted of father and mother and two sons, Stephen and Frank, and two daughters, Katie and Lena. They were blue-eyed, flaxen-haired, red-cheeked people, and friendly to a degree.

The Neubecker boys had called on the Beaumonts shortly after locating their land, and intercourse between the families soon became frequent. They were the nearest settlers on that side of the river.

The Beaumont home seemed to have a special attraction for Stephen Neubecker, and it was not long before it became evident in what that attraction con-sisted. Alice Beaumont at that period was 18 years of age, of medium height, dark-eyed and finely-chiselled features, a firm mouth and chin, and the whole surmounted by a wealth of dark-brown hair. Hers was a happy and cheerful nature. She and Stephen were the best of friends, chatted, joked and played games of dominoes and checkers, but she would not let it go beyond that. At Stephen's frequent remonstrances at being held at arm's-length she would laughingly reply :

" Now, Stephen ! We are friends. Let us remain so. Let well enough alone and do not spoil matters." She would never let matters go beyond that stage. At the dances held after " raisings " and " logging bees " she did not favour Stephen above any of the other young men of the settlement.

CHAPTER XIII.

BIRDS OF A FEATHER FLOCK TOGETHER.

THE Census of 1861 gave the population of Bruce County as 27,499. Also it gave the percentage of Race and Religions :—

Races.

					Per cent.
Canadian Birth	...	...	...	...	59
Scotch ,,	...	...	...	...	19
Irish ,,	...	...	...	...	11
English ,,	...	...	...	...	5
German ,,	...	...	...	...	4
United States Birth	...	...	...	...	1
All other Births	...	...	...	...	1
					100

Religious Persuasion.

					Per cent.
Presbyterians	...	...	...	...	44
Church of England	...	...	...	...	18
Methodists	...	...	...	...	16
Catholics	...	...	...	...	12
Baptists	...	...	...	...	4
Lutheran	...	...	...	...	2
Other Denominations	...	...	...	...	4
					100

Nationalities of the Queen's Bush.

Scotch Lowlanders	1. In Normanby Township	,,	Lowland Scotch, **Irish,** Germans.
	2. In Egremont	,,	Lowland Scotch
	3. In Glenelg	,,	Lowland Scotch, Irish.
	4. In Brant	,,	Lowland Scotch, Germans.
	5. In Culross	,,	Lowland Scotch, **High**land Scotch.
	6. In Bruce	,,	Lowland Scotch.
	7. In Arran	,,	Lowland Scotch.
	8. In Kincardine	,,	Lowland Scotch.
	9. In Saugeen	,,	Lowland Scotch, Germans.
Scotch Highlanders	1. In Culross Township		In the Alps.
	2. In S. Kinloss	,,	Gaelic-speaking Presbyterians.
	3. In Huron	,,	Isle of Lewis Settlement.
	4. In Elderslie	,,	Colonsay Settlement.
Germans	1. In Carrick Township		Formosa, Carlsruhe.
	2. In Culross	,,	N.E. part.
	3. In Saugeen	,,	Mennonites.
	4. In Brant	,,	E. & N.E. Elmwood.
	5. In Normanby	,,	Western Half.
	6. In Bentinck	,,	Hanover.
Irish	1. In Normanby Township		Centre, Ayton.
	2. In Glenelg	,,	Centre.
	3. In Greenock	,,	N.E. Chepstow.
	4. In Brant	,,	N.E. part.
	5. In Kinloss	,,	Holyrood.
French	1. In Greenock Township		Riversdale.
Negro	1. In Normanby Township		

In the settlement of the " Queen's Bush " people of one nationality or of one religious belief frequently located in colonies. This afforded mutual help and protection and engendered a kindred feeling. New settlers coming in felt that a bond of sympathy for them would exist in the ranks of their countrymen, or co-religionists—that they were not amongst an alien race or creed.

SCOTSMAN.

GERMAN.

IRISHMAN.

FRENCHMAN.

As settlement grew, these blocks acquired distinctive appellations—the Scotch block in Normanby Township; the Scotch settlements in Glenelg, Egremont and Brant Townships; the French Settlement in Greenock

Township; the Highland Settlement in the Alps of Culross; the Lewis Settlement in Huron Township; the Colonsay Settlement in Elderslie; the Irish Settlements in Glenelg; Normanby and Greenock; the German Settlements of Carrick, Brant, Culross, Saugeen, Normanby and Bentinck Townships. Of all these settlements, those of the Scots were most numerous. These were mainly Lowlanders from the South—Dumfries and Roxburghshires, Berwick and Lanarkshires, but many were Highlanders chiefly from the Western Isles of Scotland—from Arran and Islay, from Coll and Tiree, from Ross and Cromarty, and from Argyll and from Lewis in the outer Hebrides; and still another was the Colonsay and Argyll settlement in Elderslie N.E. of Paisley in the year 1853.

The Lowland Scotsman, the Highlander, the Irishman, the Frenchman, the German—they all dribbled into the " Bush " from every direction. The great majority came from the older parts of the Province of Upper Canada, where, as recent emigrants, they had been employed either as farm helps or as navvies in building the recently constructed Grand Trunk, the Great Western, or the Buffalo and Goderich Railroads.

The Scot is clannish, but is fair dealing and honest. He does not wish to take advantage of another, but he wants his own, and all of his own, in his dealings with his fellow-man. He is fond of music and of everything which redounds to the credit of his native land. He has a feeling of superiority—though not always expressed—over other nationalities. The manners and customs of his forefathers and of his native Scotland he upholds with undying vigour. Hogmanay or Watchnight and Burns' birthday are the two chief celebrations of his year.

" Get up, guid wife, and shake your feathers,
  Ye needna think that we are beggars,
  For we have only come to say,
  Please give to us our Hogmanay ! "

" We are but bairns come to play,
  Get up and give us our Hogmanay ! "

The Highlanders, on the other hand, were less "canny" than the Lowlanders. Their nature more resembled the Irish, and this no doubt because of their Celtic stock. These men from the Western Mainland and from the Western Isles of Scotland were mainly fishermen and sailors accustomed to the sea. They were therefore little adapted to hew out a home from the virgin forest in a new land and on a new Continent, and as a consequence did not make the same progress in their first few years of settlement in the Canadian Bush as their neighbours from the older parts of the Province of Upper Canada, who, born to, or long inured to, farming in a " bush " country quickly forged ahead.

But mainly these fishermen persisted, and in time they and their sons attained that competence their labours deserved. But always their thoughts recurred to the homes they had left across the sea and from which many of them had been exiled.

" From the lonely shieling on the misty Island,
  Mountains divide them and a world of seas,
  But their thoughts are true, their hearts are Hielan',
  And they behold in dreams the Hebrides ! "

The Lewis Settlement—from the Isle of Lewis in the outer Hebrides—in the centre of Huron Township, Bruce County, in the fall of 1852 was one of the largest of these " block " settlements in the " Queen's Bush." They had been exiled from their croftings by their landlord, Sir James Matheson, and probably to make the evictions less heartless a free passage was given them to Canada.

Two shiploads of these people left Stornoway, in the Isle of Lewis, in two sailing ships bound for America in 1851, and after a stormy passage across the Atlantic, landed in Quebec in August of that year.

In Quebec they divided, the majority going to the County of Compton in the eastern townships tributary to Sherbrooke. The remainder went on to Montreal by boat, and thence also by boat to Hamilton, where they disembarked, many to work upon the Great Western Railway, which was then a-building.

In the summer of 1852 these gathered at Goderich, and from there all moved to Huron Township, in the County of Bruce, and founded the Lewis Settlement in the centre of that township. They numbered 109 families—Gaelic was their mother tongue. They were the settlement of the Macs—McDonalds, McLays, McLeods, McLennans, McLeans, McIvens, McFarlanes, &c., &c., but the McDonalds were the chief.

It is related of these McDonalds, that the Johns and the Donalds were so numerous that in the early days in one S.S.—No. 5—the teacher was obliged to differentiate the Johns from one another by affixing the letters of the alphabet to the Christian name—thus, John A., John B. until he reached John U. before he exhausted the Johns, and that the Donalds required a similar treatment.

The groups of Irish settlements were not so numerous as the Scotch, but there were a number of them. The Irish settlement of Normanby was the most numerous

of these. Also the Irish settlement, in the centre of
Glenelg Township, was a numerous one, while there
was a large Irish settlement in Greenock Township
around Chepstow, and one also in N.E. Brant before
being displaced by the Germans. There were also
scattered Irish settlers in South Kinloss and Culross
Townships. For the rest of the " Queen's Bush," the
Irish formed about 11% of the population mixed in with
the other nationalities.

Almost every County and every Province in Ireland
was represented by the Irish settlers of the " Queen's
Bush," the North and the South. From Wexford and
from Kilkenny, from Cork and Tipperary, from
Killarney and from Limerick, from Kildare and King's
County, from Mayo and Sligo and Armagh, from
County Down and Fermanagh, from the wilds of
Galway on the West to County Dublin on the East.

The failure of the potato crop of 1847-8 had driven
many thousands of these people from the land of their
birth, to seek new homes across the Western Ocean.

Proud, sociable, easy-going, hospitable to a degree,
friendly, trustful, these people lacked the steady
industry of the Scot, and their one besetting vice—like
that of the Scot, but unlike the latter they could not
control the desire—was their appetite for liquor.

In the race to affluence, many of the Irish became
displaced by the more industrious German. This is
particularly so in parts of Brant and Normanby
Townships.

The Germans settled in great numbers in the
" Queen's Bush." They were a thrifty race, and they
flocked to a region where the land was good. Good
soil, good water and good timber were the three
attractions which brought these people to the " Bush."

Amongst the first of these settlers were the Mennonites, who settled in Saugeen Township, and they, like most of the other settlers of this and the neighbouring townships, found entrance thereto by the floating highway —the Saugeen River—from Durham. A large colony of Mennonites settled in the eastern part of Brant Township in the vicinity of the present Elmwood. Central Brant had also a large influx of Mecklenburg Germans from the north of Germany. Carrick was one of the last townships in Bruce County to be surveyed, and upon the finish of the survey and being thrown open was almost at once settled, mostly by Germans, due to the reports of its good soil and good water. In 1854 a large colony of Germans from Alsace settled at Formosa, in the north-western part of the township, and a colony from Baden, Germany, in north-eastern Carrick at Carlsruhe.

There were some scattered negroes in Normanby and Artemesia Townships, and quite a large number located in Sydenham Township.

CHAPTER XIV.

THE LOG HOME IN THE BACKWOODS.

THE following week preparations went forward for building a home. In the meantime the cook-house on the raft had been removed to the shore and served as an addition to the shanty.

Mr. Beaumont and the boys began the felling of trees. The oxen were used to drag the timbers to the central part of the glade where the log house was to be erected. The timber was dressed upon one side only—the inner—whilst the outer was left with its bark on. The corners were notched to dovetail into each other. A large excavation was first made in the ground for a cellar, and the foundation logs of the house placed around it. In this the oxen proved of great service, also in the raising of the logs on to the walls by means of skids and chains. Slowly the walls attained a proper height and rafters were laid on; shingles made from split cedar blocks formed the roof.

A fireplace, built of clay, plastered on a wicker frame, was built at one end of the house, and a floor of split basswood was laid down. A door of the same material was hung, and a couple of openings made to serve as windows to admit light. The spaces between the logs were then filled in by " chinking." This was done by wedging triangular cedar blocks into the spaces between the logs and plastering over with clay. A tea kettle, a baking pot (an iron pot with a lid called a Dutch oven), and a frying pan formed the cooking utensils of the family.

A table, some rough chairs, together with four bedsteads, all made with the rough tools of the settlers, formed the furnishings below-stairs, while a rude ladder at one end of the room led upstairs, where the boys had their sleeping quarters.

A root house for vegetables was also built, an oblong excavation in the ground was dug to a depth of $2\frac{1}{2}$ feet and 10 feet wide by 20 feet long, and a rough framework with sloping sides built over it, and the whole covered with earth to a depth of 2 feet or more. It had a wooden door at one end which served for entrance. The structure served to protect the roots and potatoes from the frosts of winter.

A stable built of logs served as a rough shelter for the cattle, and Beaver Meadow hay cut in quantity from neighbouring Beaver Meadows and built in stacks near the stable served as fodder. Oftentimes in the following winter the snow penetrated the chinks between the logs in the rough stable, and morning found the animals covered white with snow.

The work progressed as the days went on. Finally, the house was finished and the family moved into it, and that night celebrated by a gathering of some of the scattered settlers in a " house warming." " Bush " problems were discussed by the elders, while the younger people engaged in a dance. A hot supper followed, and the party disbanded with best wishes for many years of happiness in the new home.

It was a crude home, and comforts were but few, but as time went on these were added to; but it also had its advantages. It was surrounded by a majestic forest, a noble river ran by its doorway, the pure air and fertile soil gave it a beauty all its own.

The wild forest was ploughed—roughly, 'tis true,

because of the myriad roots—by the oxen, and potatoes and some wheat and oats were planted and sown. A barrel was made and sunk at the near-by spring for water.

Deer, duck and partridge were plentiful. The family never lacked for fresh meat, and the river teemed with excellent fish. Still more settlers kept pouring in : the Smiths, Bacons, Eckfords and Gordons and many of their old neighbours from Woolwich Township. Amongst the latter was the Haag family. Johnny Haag was still of the same contradictory nature as of yore. As a man he was what he had been as a boy He now gambled, drank and swore in spells, and in spells, when he became sober, repented his debauches. He was a " heart ache " to his aged father, Gottlieb Haag, whose upright life and Christian character abhorred drunkenness and gambling. Johnny had called on the Beaumonts on the first arrival of his family in the township. Alice Beaumont received him with smiles and gladness. She hoped he had reformed his ways and was the old good-hearted playmate of her school days. But his bloodshot eyes and bloated face chilled her heart with misgiving.

" I am well, Alice. I only came to this ' bush ' because you are here," he said. " Why won't you marry me, Alice, and we will settle down on a bush farm, where you will be near your own people and near your mother ? I am sure I can make you happy, and it would be paradise for me !"

" Hush, Jack ! You shouldn't talk so. I will never marry. I am going to remain single and look after mother," said Alice.

" More likely look after Steve Neubecker ! Or is it

George Gordon?'' exclaimed Jack, with a dark look on his face.

" You have no right to make such remarks, Mr. Jack Haag! My friends are of my own choosing, and do not come to this house again until you can speak and behave like a gentleman!'' and the enraged girl turned away from him to attend to her housework.

"Forgive me, Alice. I am sorry. It is my jealous nature. But it shows you how much I think of you," said Haag, contritely.

Summer came, bloomed, blossomed and waned, and the forest glade produced a bounteous supply of potatoes; wild berries also came in profusion; raspberries, strawberries and black- and thimble-berries, as also came wild red plums. Of these latter Mrs. Beaumont made a delectable jelly. In September came wild elderberries of which wine and jam were made.

The principal roads through the settlement were being opened up. No longer had the traveller to watch the "blaze" on the trees to follow his path. Roads were chopped through the forest of a uniform width of 66 feet or 1 chain, the centre 16 feet of which the trees were cut off level with the roadway and hauled to one side. For the other 50 feet the trees were allowed to remain where they fell on either side of the highway.

Logging Bees, Raising Bees and Quilting Bees became frequent in the settlement. With September came the cutting of the grain—wheat and oats. This was done with the "cradle," a variety of scythe or sickle, with four or five wooden fingers above the knife, the whole attached to a handle.

The grain when cut was laid in a "windrow" behind the cutter, with the heads lying all one way. This was then raked in bundles, and the latter tied with its own straw for a band. For threshing out the grain a space of ground was cleared of its sod cover, well pounded to pack the soil and form a firm bottom, and upon this the sheaves of grain were laid, and after cutting open the bands " flails " were then used by the men to thresh out the grain.

Sometimes the oxen were driven over this " threshing floor " backwards and forwards and roundabout until finally all the straw was free of its grain, and was then gathered up and placed aside, while the difficult part of separating the grain from the chaff was begun. This was usually done with a hand sieve or weht, and on a windy day. The shaker filled his sieve with grain and chaff, which he shook, the wind blowing the chaff to one side. This tedious labour resulted in wheat mixed with considerable chaff and weed seeds.

With the advent of autumn the forest began changing her dress, the bright green of the maple, the beech and the elm began turning to crimson and gold, and the leaves to silently detach themselves from the parent stem and flutter gently down, a stern reminder of the Grim Visitor—Winter, who was on his way. Roots and vegetables were stored away in cellar and root house, the dwelling house banked up with earth for two feet all around its foundation, and all preparations made to put in the first winter in the " Bush."

With the first snow of autumn John Beaumont made a rough jumper from ironwood saplings, and hitching the oxen to it loaded a few bags of wheat, to make his first journey to the Grist Mill at Durham for flour, 25 to 30 miles away and to the westward, and over the forest roads or " blazes."

This entailed an absence of four or five days : a day and a half to make the outward trip, the same to return,

and a day or a day and a half to await one's turn for
a grist at the mill, for outside Durham there was no
other mill nearer than that at the mouth of the Penetangore, 30 to 40 miles away, and through the dense
forest on the shores of Lake Huron.

The story is told of an early settler of Carrick Township in this tract that, upon reaching Durham, on the
second day of his journey to the mill with a grist, and
being footsore and hungry after his weary tramp
through the woods and having no money to buy a meal
at the only tavern in the town, he awaited his turn for
his grist until night, and that, when finally made, he
turned back the lips of the bag, and pouring some water
upon the top of the flour, kneaded it into scones, which
he baked on the top of the miller's stove used for heating the mill, and so appeased his hunger. Such were
some of the hardships of the men who settled in the
" Queen's Bush."

In going to and returning from the mill the pioneer
endeavoured to reach some settler's shanty ere night
had fallen. In those days in the " Bush " open-handed
hospitality was the rule. The latch string on the
settler's door ever hung out a welcome to the wayfarer.

Should night overtake him away from a clearing he
first unloosed his oxen from the jumper, hobbled them
by means of a short strap buckled to their front ankles
to prevent straying or a stampede in case of howls from
a pack of wolves, made a camp-fire and built
himself a " lean-to," under which he crept, rolling
himself in a blanket and lying upon hemlock boughs,
and so passed the night until daybreak, when he resumed
his way.

In these journeys for flour usually three or four

adjoining settlers joined forces for companionship and help in case of a breakdown.

In the very early days before roadways were chopped out, and when the way was a track following a line of " blazed " trees, another method was used. A short yoke with two holes bored in it was fitted on to the horns of the ox. From this a rope led backwards to a small " jumper " made with upturned runners, and upon which two or three bags of wheat were placed, and with this primitive conveyance the forest pathways were negotiated, and the family back in the " Bush " supplied with the much needed flour.

The outdoor life, the rough labour, the plain but nutritious food developed a rugged health in these early pioneers, and without their knowing anything about vitamins, chiropractic or Christian science, carried them well past the three-score and ten years, the allotted span of human life. Many of these early settlers lived to be 80 and 90 years of age.

To chop down 5 acres of standing hardwood timber was the usual allotment of a backwoodsman's winter labour. John Beaumont was anxious to enlarge his clearing for the following spring seeding. So that fall he, with Guy and Alex, began their winter's work upon the standing timber.

The merry sound of the woodman's axe was heard ringing through the forest aisles morning, noon and evening in the woods adjacent to the clearing. The trees were felled with method, that is, as much as possible in piles to facilitate logging in the spring.

The work went on without flagging. Sore hands and sore backs were the share of the boys until they became expert in the use of the axe, and every evening the grindstone standing in front of the door on its high frame of four legs was busy sharpening the axes for the following day's work.

Gradually the clearing enlarged until by spring full 10 acres had been added to that of the original forest glade upon whose shore they had landed from their raft in the preceding May.

And the timber that was then destroyed! How we should value it now! Then it was an encumbrance to be gotten rid of as quickly as possible—the lordly pine, the monarch of the forest trees, the towering elm, the beautiful bird's-eye maple, and the hardy beech all felled to form a holocaust the following spring, to make room for the lowly wheat which was to follow and which was to rule the world.

CHAPTER XV.

THE COON HUNT AND PIGEON ROOST.

LATE one fall the Indians—Kubassey, Niwash and Chief Madawaygosh—with their squaws came up river on a hunting and trapping expedition. They camped in Beaumont's woods close to the river. Here in a sylvan glen, surrounded by the dark forest, they erected their wigwams and built their camp fires. While the bucks hunted and trapped the squaws made baskets and bead work.

The baskets were of 4- and 6-quart size with handles, and made of thin split elm with blue and red lines of colouring upon their sides. Sometimes they made large woven clothes baskets of the same material. These found ready purchasers amongst the settlers. The bead work was chiefly that done upon moccasins and ornamental purses made of fine tanned doeskin. The beads themselves were of blue, red and yellow tint.

The Indians remained in this camp for a month or six weeks until ice had formed in the river and streams.

Here the neighbouring farmer lads gathered at evenings, bringing delicacies in the shape of loaves of bread, cakes or pies, and received in return a present of perhaps a tanned muskrat skin suitable for making a winter cap, or of a mink skin suitable for a lady's cap or muff, and to listen to the Indian tales and legends.

At one of these gatherings Kubassey told the young men of the Indian method of coon hunting, and proposed a coon hunt for the next evening. The proposition was eagerly accepted.

Accordingly, the young men gathered early the next evening at the Indian camp, armed with shot-guns and lanterns, for Kubassey had instructed them to bring along these latter, and also a couple of empty sacks.

Guy and Alex Beaumont, Steve Neubecker, Jack Haag and Pat Godfrey, and one or two other neighbouring homesteaders formed the party with the Indians. Followed by a couple of hounds—Bess and Sport—belonging to Guy Beaumont, the party set out into the woods leading back from the river. The hounds quickly disappeared amongst the trees and underbrush. Presently Bess "gave tongue," making the woods resound with the clamour, and was quickly joined by Sport.

The party quickly made their way through the undergrowth, and came out in an opening in which were a few scattered trees.

At the foot of one of these trees—an old maple with some dead limbs hanging from its top—the hounds had gathered, and were sitting on their haunches gazing upwards or racing around the tree, making frantic leaps upwards and giving voice to a deep-toned baying.

The party—guns at the "ready"—now gathered gathered around the maple, but were unable to see anything in the shape of a racoon, either on the trunk of the tree or upon any of its limbs.

"Give Peter lantern," said Niwash, "he find coon," and taking a lantern from Guy held it high above his head, gazing upwards and at the same time circling the tree.

Stopping suddenly, he exclaimed "Here your coon!" pointing upwards, where in the crotch of a tree, perhaps twenty-five feet from the ground, two glaring sheen-like balls—from the coon's eyes—reflected the lantern's light.

Pointing this out to Guy, who was at the Indian's side, Guy raised his gun and fired, when a large fat coon falling downwards plumped upon the ground at their feet. The hounds quickly pounced upon it, but were driven off by Guy, who, picking up the dead coon, slung it over his shoulders.

The hounds were then started into the woods once more, and presently began baying around another tree. This time Guy determined to imitate the Indian's trick of locating the coon, and holding the lantern on the top of his own head, but at an angle so that its light would be directed upwards, while his own eyes were in shadow, began slowly circling the tree at whose base the hounds were clamouring.

Presently he saw the sheen-like glare of two eye-balls flashing down upon him, and calling to his brother Alex, pointed it out. Alex fired at the reflection, but no coon came tumbling down, as in the first instance, also the glaring eyes had disappeared, so Alex fired another shot in the same general direction as the first, but without result.

Guy circled with the light again, but obtained no reflection. A couple of more shots were fired at where the eyes had been seen, but without result.

"Coon dead," declared Kubassey, "lodged in tree. Must climb tree and bring down."

"Let me do it," said Jack Haag. "I am a good climber," and so saying he embraced the tree—shinning up to its lower branches—by which means he quickly raised himself up, and climbing from branch to branch, presently reached the crotch where the coon had laid.

Here, after a pause, he pulled out the dead coon, and calling out " Look out below !" cast it downwards.

Examining the place where the coon had laid, Haag discovered a large hole in the main trunk of the tree, and putting in his hand it at once came in contact with warm fur. Grasping this, he pulled out what proved to be a young racoon.

" Say, boys, there's a nest of young coons up here !" he called. " This tree is hollow. One of you fellows come up here with one of those sacks to hold the coons."

Alex Beaumont hastily clambered up the tree with a sack, into which Haag placed four young coons, one after the other, which he drew from out the nest in the trunk.

Haag then put his hand into the hole for the fifth time, but with a howl and a jerk hastily withdrew it, with a large coon—the mother—attached to the member, which the cornered animal had bitten.

With a yell Jack Haag attempted to detach the racoon from his hand, and in his wild efforts to liberate himself detached both himself and the coon from the limb upon which he sat, and man and coon breaking through the maple limbs, fell heavily to the earth, where the dogs quickly pounced on the wild animal and killed it.

Yells of laughter greeted Haag, who sat upon the ground nursing his wounded hand which the coon had bitten. " I guess you caught a Tartar that time, Jack !" cried Guy Beaumont.

On their homeward journey from the coon hunt, and on passing through a dense piece of woods a great fluttering in the branches overhead was heard,

mingled with the sound of breaking branches and now
and again the crash of a falling body.

Calling for the lantern, Guy rushed forward and
found the fluttering objects which had crashed downwards to be wild pigeons. These on approaching
became bewildered with the lantern light and fluttered
around amongst the leaves and brushwood.

The coon party had stumbled upon a pigeon roost.
The leaves below the trees were covered with pigeon
eggs, and on holding the lantern aloft strings of wild
pigeons could be seen sitting side by side on the
branches of the trees, craning their necks from side to
side, viewing the unusual appearance of a light in the
forest.

Long poles were cut down by the boys and trimmed,
and many of the birds knocked from their roosts and
fell to the earth, where they were secured.

"Only what we can use, boys," said Guy. "No
useless slaughter. Some can be salted and kept for
food, but not too many, or there will be waste."

Each member of the party therefore loaded himself
with as many dead pigeons as he thought he could
conveniently carry, and these, with a supply of pigons'
eggs and the dead coons in bags, formed the spoils of
the Night Hunt of the Coon Party.

CHAPTER XVI.

Jealousy.

Dances were of frequent occurrence in the new settlement. The young people of the Beaumont household had been clamouring for some time for a dance.

The dance they had had at their house-warming had been a tame affair, and only a limited number of friends had been invited thereto, but now Guy and the boys, Alex and Jack, Alice and Mary were keen to hold one, as many of their neighbours had already done, and to which they had been invited and had participated. Finally Mr. and Mrs. Beaumont gave their consent.

Invitations therefore went out to all the neighbours that a general gathering was to be held. The Neubeckers, Haags, Everetts, Godfreys, Lamonts, Boultons, Smiths, Gordons—in fact, all the young people of that part of the township were invited. Musicians—violin and bass—were secured, and refreshments on a large scale were prepared.

The eventful evening came at last. Bevies of young ladies in ribbons and flounces arrived early, many of them escorted by their cavaliers—pretty Fanny Lamont; dark-haired, dark-eyed and mischievous Bernice Boulton; the blue-eyed, rosy-cheeked, flaxen-haired Neubecker girls—Rosie and Katie; demure Margaret Stewart; the witching Mary Gordon; the charming Lucy Everett, besides many another of the youth and beauty of the settlements; while Alice Beaumont, her hair dressed in a coil at the back of her head, her dark, expressive eyes, her finely-chiselled features and her regal bearing, left no doubt she was a " Backwoods Queen " and the " Belle of the Ball."

Mr. and Mrs. Beaumont mingled with the throng—a hearty handshake and a kindly greeting for each and everyone.

Though it was late fall the night—as the day had been—was very warm. It was a touch of Indian summer, that glorious time in the Canadian woods when the trees stand silent, with drooping leaves, sorrowing as it were at the change that was to come; and with changing colours turning to crimson and gold and silently dropping to the earth, to form a coat of many colours to deck its bosom; and when a solemn stillness reigned through the forest aisles, which loomed dim in the smoky hazy, sunlit atmosphere.

On Stephen's first arrival at the Beaumonts that evening he had gone through the groups of visitors in search of Miss Alice, and at last finding her surrounded by a group of young men, had shaken hands and had whispered in her ear :

" Alice, you must give me two dances to-night. One a quadrille and the other a waltz. I have been counting on them, so do not say no."

" Well, Stephen, as it's you, I suppose I'll have to," replied the girl, smiling archly at her admirer. Jack Haag had observed this whispered conference between Stephen and Alice, and the Devil of Jealousy flamed in his breast.

Going over to Miss Alice, he also asked for the favour of three dances for the night—a waltz, a schottische and a quadrille.

" Oh, but I can't do that, Jack!" she replied. " I

mustn't be monopolized by any one guest. I can only give you one dance, Jack, and that a quadrille, and only after the dance gets well under way."

With this Haag had to be content and withdrew, muttering curses under his breath, while Alice flitted away to welcome some newly-arrived guests. Haag determined, if possible, to lower Steve in Alice's estimation at any cost, so going outside he joined a group of young men—Pat Godfrey, Dick Everett, Tom Boulton and others—and producing a flask of liquor, said :

" Here, boys ! Take something to put ginger into your dancing !" and passed the flask to Pat Godfrey. The latter put the bottle to his lips and drank, but found the liquor to be too fiery and so did not swallow much, but passed the bottle on to Ed. Boulton and then the others, after which it was returned to Haag.

Just then Stephen Neubecker emerged from the doorway and joined the group, when Haag handed him the flask, saying :

" Here, Steve, we've just been taking a nip. Have a snifter ?" and he put the flask in Steve's hands. The latter demurred at first, but one of the boys saying " Be a sport, Steve !" raised the bottle to his lips and drank. It was fiery stuff, being French cognac brandy, and made Steve splutter and partially lose his breath.

The musicians had by now again tuned up and dancing began within the house. The young men returned thereto. Stephen endeavoured to find Alice, and on succeeding and the floor manager calling out " Partners for a quadrille," led out that young lady, and they took their places in a set. At the conclusion of the dance Stephen led his partner to a seat, and stooping, whispered in her ear that he was coming for the waltz—the dance after the next one. " No, no, Stephen!" cried Alice. " That is too soon. We mustn't dance too often. It will excite comment. Come in an hour and I will give you the waltz."

Stephen withdrew to chat with some of his neighbours and wait for his hour to elapse. For poor simple-hearted Stephen there was only one girl at the dance. Of all the bevy of youth and beauty who had assembled there that night, there was one, and only one, who had ever stirred his heart, and that was Miss Alice. Passing around the room he greeted a friend here and there, for Stephen was a general favourite, and finding the heat of the room too great, he passed out of the doorway at the front of the house. Here, on the sward, he found assembled a group of young men from the dance room, and discovered several of them had bottles of beer in their hands, from which they took occasional drinks.

" Come here, Steve! Here's something to cool you off. Have a bottle of beer!" cried Jack Haag, who going to a near-by bush and picking out a bottle from a compartment box labelled " Schiltz's Beer," handed it to Stephen.

Stephen had been heated up in the dance and was thirsty, so removing the cork, he placed the bottle to his lips and emptied it of its contents, returning the empty flask to Haag and thanking him. The latter smiled knowingly and said, " Tasted pretty good, Steve? That sure is the stuff!" and placed the empty bottle back in the box.

Presently Steve began to feel greatly exhilarated. His spirits soared. No labour so hard, no conditions so difficult he could not accomplish. His step grew lighter, he felt he could dance the whole night through without fatigue, and this brought the thought to his mind of his engagement with Miss Alice for a waltz.

Returning with unsteady footsteps to the dance room, he passed around the seated onlookers until he found Miss Alice, and said :

"Now, Miss Alice, this is our waltz," and crooking his left arm held it out to her. The musicians had just struck up a waltz, so Alice arose, and taking Steve's arm, advanced into the centre of the room, where other couples had already taken their places and had begun circling away down the room to the strains of the " Blue Danube."

As Alice and Steve began circling in the waltz Steve's steps became somewhat uncertain, which Alice put down to shyness and endeavoured to reassure him, but presently, in doing a circle somewhat more vigorous than any of its predecessors, Stephen lost his grasp of his partner and sprawled full length upon his back upon the floor, where he lay staring upwards with a vacuous smile at his partner.

The girl stood, a red blush mounting from her neck to her face, staring with amazement and embarrassment at the figure lying on the floor before her.

" Stephen, Stephen, get up !" she cried.

" Mish Alish, I'msh very shorry I tripped mineshelf ! This floorsh ish very unevensh !" said Steve.

Every eye in the room was now turned upon the couple in the centre of the floor. The other waltzers had stopped dancing to gaze in wonder at the prostrate man. The musicians also had ceased playing. The mortified girl, red, embarrassed and ashamed, stood in silent misery by the prostrate figure. With a bound Guy Beaumont sprang from his seat by the wall, where he had been exchanging repartees with pretty Bernice

Boulton, and was instantly at his sister's side, and taking her by the arm, said, "Come, Alice," and led her to his mother at one end of the room.

Some of the young men—Boulton, Everett, Godfrey, and Jack Haag, with his malevolent smile—now rushed forwards, and taking Steve's arms raised him to a sitting position, whence he was raised to his feet, but as he was quite unable to walk he was supported out of the doorway to a near-by tree, where he was placed with his back against it, sitting upon the grass, when he exclaimed :

"Boysh, I'm alrish. I can dansh the whole nitsh through."

Jack Haag gave a guffaw, whilst Ed. Boulton looked sharply at Stephen.

"Steve," he said, "how many bottles of that beer did you drink? Answer me."

"Onsh, Ed. But that was nossing. I could drinksh a dozen bottlsh of that stuffsh and not hurt mush. Slopsh! Slopsh!" muttered the drunken man.

At this juncture Jim Bacon drew Ed. to one side and imparted the information that he had half an hour previously seen Jack Haag empty the brandy flask he carried into a beer bottle and then fill the latter with beer, cork the bottle, and carefully replace it in a certain corner of the beer box.

"The measly hound!" said Ed. Boulton. "Why did he do that?"

"Oh, probably to play a joke on Steve, or it may have had a deeper meaning," replied Bacon.

Alice had in the meantime retired to her room, followed by the pitying glances of all the young ladies, where she had a good cry. Presently her mother burst into the room.

" Hoity toity ! Are you crying for that drunken Steve Neubecker, who shamed you before all the people ? Never shall he be invited into this house again !" cried the enraged matron.

" Oh, mother, I don't believe it was Stephen's fault. There must be some mistake !" pleaded the girl.

" Mistake nothing ! Wasn't he drunk ? He could only get drunk by drinking. How else ? I hope he goes home and never shows his face here again !" exclaimed the angered mother. " Stop crying. Have some pride about you. Go on down and face your guests and go on with the dancing. You have nothing to feel ashamed about !" cried the angered mother, and shoved the girl before her from the room.

Alice thereupon returned to the dance room, took her part as if nothing had happened, and accepted every offer to dance, and, but for her heightened colour, no one would think she was the embarrassed, shamed and mortified girl of an hour previous.

The dance continued until the wee small hours of morning, when all the neighbours dispersed to their homes, some of the young men assisting Steve to his home, where he was helped to bed.

CHAPTER XVII.

WILD HONEY.

ONE day in early September Peter Niwash called at the Beaumont Homestead and asked for Miss Alice. Mrs. Beaumont invited him into the kitchen, gave him a lunch of bread, maple syrup and tea, and went to call Alice. Presently Alice entered the room.

" Why, how do you do, Peter?" she cried. " You are quite a stranger here. You haven't been to see us since last spring," cried the girl.

The Chippeway shook his head, and waving his hand to the North, exclaimed :

" No. Far away all summer at Manitoulin."

" So! And where is your squaw, ' Bright Eyes,' Peter? and your little papoose, Panginini? [little man]. They are not with you?" said Alice.

" No, Sagin " (at the mouth), replied Peter, and he waved down river.

" Young squaw like honey?" said Peter. " Wild bee make honey in tree. Peter take ' Wild Rose ' "— for such the Indians had named the girl—" to tree."

" Why, yes," said Alice, " that would be very nice. The boys and I will go with you this afternoon, Peter, and get some."

Accordingly that afternoon Alice, Mary, Guy and Alex, carrying a couple of pails for the sweets, left in company with Peter for the woods and for the bee tree : Peter took along an axe, and travelled at first in a northerly direction, away from the river. After traversing a quarter of a mile of forest, he led the party to the left or westwards for a short distance into Philip Neubecker's woods, where a small "swale" or piece of swampy ground opened out. This swale was surrounded by trees—beech and maple, elm and basswood and hemlock. Before one of these trees, a big basswood, the Indian stopped and struck the back of the axe against the tree.

At once a dull humming noise was heard, and Peter, looking up at the tree and then at his companions, said :

"Big tree !   Much honey !" and gave the axe to Guy and motioned him to chop. Guy quickly plied the axe, making the chips fly in all directions, and presently a premonitory crack proclaimed the tree was falling.

It fell outwards into the swale with a resounding crash, splitting open in so doing, and liberating hundreds of angry bees, and disclosing at the same time the upper half of the tree filled with luscious honeycombs, from which now exuded the glittering nectar.

At once the party were surrounded by the angry insects, and a general scatteration into the surrounding woods occurred. Cries of pain, the slapping of hands and hats to drive away the vicious insects began. The party was completely and instantly routed. Even Peter Niwash's tough skin was not proof against the bee stings, and he, too, took refuge in the surrounding woods.

"I declare my neck and face are full of stings. Oh, we will not get any honey now. What shall we do now, Peter?" cried Alice, addressing the Indian.

"Go home. Get more pails for honey. We come back, make smoke and drive bees away," was the Indian's answer.

Poor Mary, who had received many stings, was now bathing her face in a near-by pool of water. Her face was so swollen from stings that her eyes were almost closed.

"Oh, Alice, my face is dreadful sore! And I lost my straw hat back there at the honey, and I daren't go back to get it," said Mary.

The bees were still buzzing angrily about the fallen tree.

"Never mind, Mary," replied the sister. "When we reach home we will grease your face with racoon oil. That will stop the pain of the stings, and when we return for the honey and smoke off the bees you can recover your hat."

The party then returned slowly to the Beaumont homestead, exciting gales of laughter from Mr. and Mrs. Beaumont by the swollen and ludicrous appearance of their faces.

These were quickly bathed in cold water and anointed with the "coon oil," and in the course of an hour or so all were again on their way back to the honey tree, bearing along with them a small tub to hold the honey.

On reaching the edge of the swale a second time, what was their astonishment to behold a form which at first sight they took to be a man standing by the bee tree, and with Mary's straw hat perched rakishly on his head, busily engaged in what appeared to the onlookers to be the act of washing his face with his hands.

On closer approach the figure proved to be a black bear who, during the absence of the party at the homestead, had smelled the honey from the neighbouring forest, and making his way to it and nosing into it, had evidently had his head covered by the angry bees, whose stings had probably driven him to roll about in the leaves covering the ground, smearing leaves and honey over his head, and in his efforts to get relief from the stings, coming in contact with Mary's hat, which adhered to Bruin's sticky head.

The bear presented a truly ludicrous appearance with the straw hat cocked over his left ear; rubbing his fore-paws against his head and body while he hopped about from place to place endeavouring to get relief from his tormentors; his head surrounded by a cloud of angry bees gave him the appearance of a drunken dancing master endeavouring to execute the figures of a laborious cotillion.

The spectators went into roars of laughter at the sight. Upon hearing this the bear paused, and sighting them made rapidly off into the surrounding forest, bearing Mary's hat with him. Peter now advanced as close as possible to the bees, who were still angrily buzzing about the honey tree, and setting fire to some brush, upon which he threw some green grass, produced a strong " smudge " which gradually enveloped the bees, stupefying and driving them away

The party now found a great deal of the honeycombs had been destroyed by the bear. Much of the honey had run out on the ground and had been lost. Still, enough honeycomb was salvaged to fill two small pails. With this the party started back for the homestead, when the Indian exclaimed :

" Wild Rose want more honey ? Peter can get more."

" How, Peter ?" exclaimed Alice.

" Come. Peter show," and going back to the prostrate basswood the Indian paused, keeping careful watch upon the ground where the honeycombs had been

shattered and where some bees were still crawling
about.

Presently a bee arose in the air and flew off in a
westward direction. This Peter watched as long as
possible until it disappeared into the distance; then
making careful note of the point where the bee was last
seen, he struck off in that direction with the laconic
"Come!" followed by Alice and Mary. On reaching
the neighbourhood of the tree where the bee was last
seen, Peter paused, and presently another bee flew past
in the same general direction upon which the first had
gone. This bee also was kept in sight until distance
had caused it to vanish, when another advance was
made. These manœuvres were gone through several
times, until finally a bee passing them flew into a knot
hole, opening high up in a hollow beech tree, a short
distance beyond them.

The party now found themselves considerably to the
westward of their own homestead and in Gottlieb
Haag's woods.

The Indian was an experienced bee hunter, with sharp
eyes and accustomed to forest ways. He had often
followed homing bees to their hives in hollow trees.

Advancing now to the tree into which the bee had
gone, he struck it smartly with the back of his axe. At
once a dull humming noise was heard. It was another
bee tree.

"Oh, I wish the boys had come with us!" said Alice.
"You will now have to chop down the tree yourself,
Peter."

"Peter can do," replied the Indian, "but first must
make smoke."

"Oh, yes. I had forgotten. Don't let us get stung
again," replied Alice.

Peter now set fire to some brush and created a dense
" smudge " around the bee tree, which he now attacked
with the axe, the girls meantime keeping up the
" smudge."

" Why, hallo! Who is chopping down our timber?"
said a voice, and Jack Haag emerged from the surrounding forest.

" Hallo, Jack!" exclaimed Alice. " Peter here has
just discovered a bee tree for us and we are going to get
some honey. You can have a share if you will chop
down the tree."

" That will be fine! I sure will!" cried Haag, and
seizing the axe from Peter, rapidly attacked the tree
while the Indian kept up a vigorous " smudge."

The tree was soon felled and split open with the axe,
and revealed its upper half filled with luscious honeycombs. The bees overpowered by the smoke quickly
flew away.

" Oh, what a sight!" exclaimed Alice, clasping her
hands. " What a lot of lovely honey, and we left the
tub at the first honey tree! We will have to go back
and get it."

" I will go along and carry it for you, Alice," said
Haag.

" All right; that's very nice of you," said Alice.
" Mary, you help Peter remove the honeycombs while
Jack and I get the tub."

The couple then struck back through Haag and
Neubecker's woods to the " swale " where the first bee
tree had been discovered, the location of which Alice
remembered fairly well. Through swamps and underbrush they pushed their way. At one place a huge
fallen elm, lying at right angles to their course,
obstructed their way.

Haag climbed on to it, and then, reaching down and seizing Alice's hands, helped her up to the top. Then, hopping down on the farther side, held out his arms and said " Jump Alice, I will catch you !"

" Oh, I don't like to. I think I can get down myself," said the girl.

" Don't be foolish. Jump !" exclaimed Haag, and at the instant, her foot slipping, Alice plumped down into Haag's outstretched arms. These he kept about the girl and embraced her, and drawing her head down upon his shoulders kissed her plump upon the lips !

The scarlet rushed to the girl's face, and with a swing of her arm she brought her open left hand against Haag's right cheek in a resounding slap, which staggered Haag and released herself.

" Jack Haag, how dare you !" exclaimed the outraged girl. " Not another step will I go with you to be insulted. Mary ! Mary !" and the girl raised a cry for her sister. " Come to me !" and the mortified girl circled the fallen elm, and with sobs began running back to her sister and the Indian.

Haag ran after her, exclaiming :

" Why, Alice, I was carried away by my feelings. I am sorry you take it so."

" Go away. Do not speak to me !" sobbed the girl.

" You would not act so if it were Steve Neubecker or George Gordon," said the nettled Haag.

" Jack Haag, if you don't leave me, I will call for the Indian to come and chastise you !" flared the angered girl. " This is not the first time you've made such remarks. I won't have it ! We are not friends any longer !" and the girl ran on to join her sister and Peter Niwash, sobbing as she ran.

"You are mine! You can't get away! I will have you! I will make you mine!" declared Haag, racing after the girl, and throwing his arm about her waist, stopped her flight. The girl turned upon him like a wild cat, striking him upon the face with her open hands and emitting shriek on shriek at the top of her voice for help.

But help was at hand. Two men broke out of the surrounding bush, guns in hand, and one of them, dropping his gun, rushed forward and dealt Haag a blow on the side of his head, staggering him and making him lose his hold on Alice. The latter now sank to the ground, her form shaken with sobs.

"What is it, Alice?" asked George Gordon, who with Stephen Neubecker were the newcomers, and who had been out together partridge shooting.

"What is the matter, Alice? Will you not tell me?" again George asked, but the girl's only reply was to sob deeper.

Turning to Haag, who had meantime recovered himself and who stood glowering, "What have you been doing to the girl, Haag?" he demanded.

"None of your business, Gordon. Are you her owner? You and Neubecker must be two of her fancy men!" brazenly declared Haag.

Barely had he uttered the words, when Gordon sprang and struck him a blow across the mouth with his open hand, shouting:

"Strip, you hound! I'll cram that lie down your throat, you slandering dog!"

The fight that followed was of short duration. Haag was no match for the backwoodsman Gordon. In a very few minutes Haag had been knocked insensible, after being well trounced.

Turning to Alice, George said : " Come, Alice, Steve and I will accompany you home to your mother," and he raised the sobbing girl up, and tenderly placing his arm about her, supported her from the spot.

Presently Haag came to, and got on his feet with a dizzy feeling and looked about him; his head ached; his breathing hurt him; his eyes became swollen, and his lips cut and bleeding, and some of his teeth loosened from their sockets by Gordon's blows.

" Curse them ! I will get even with them !" He resumed his coat and staggered off into the woods, cursing and picking his way homewards.

CHAPTER XVIII.

The Logging Bee.

Spring came with its sunshine, its balmy breezes and its warm rains. By the end of March all the snow had disappeared. The " honk-honk " of wild geese flying northwards to their feeding grounds in the Arctic was daily heard, long streams of them, with a wary old gander at their head, came up from the south. The drumming of partridges in the " swales " resounded through the woods. Wild ducks in profusion appeared on the river and streams. All nature seemed to rejoice at the change coming over the earth. The tap-tap-tap of the red-headed woodpecker, as he reamed out a hole in a dying basswood or beech, became a frequent sound. The same red-headed gentleman would pause at his work, cock his head to one side at a red squirrel, chattering his anger on a near-by maple, as with tail erected over his back he ran up and down the trunk of the tree in violent protest.

' The forest glade was again ploughed and such parts of the adjoining " slash " as could be cultivated were added thereto.

The ten acres of timber cut during the preceding winter now required to be logged into piles, so that later when dry, as the summer came it could be burned.

At the chopping during the winter the limbs of the trees had been carefully placed in piles by themselves, separate from the logs, as these would dry quicker and be burnt off sooner than the logs.

The logs had been cut into twelve- and fourteen-foot lengths, sutable for two men to handle when logging.

As before mentioned, in the felling of the trees they were as much as possible felled in heaps to facilitate logging, and others cut into 12- and 14-feet lengths, but only with an axe, never with a saw.

To clear up the slash of ten acres, John Beaumont decided to have a logging bee, and so early in June,

LOGGING BEE.

after the seeding had been finished, he went around and invited all his neighbours to the logging.

On the appointed day the settlers gathered at the homestead to the number of 50 men and about a dozen ox-teams. Each ox-team had a gang of four men allotted to it—the driver who guided the oxen, the chain man whose duty it was to fasten and unfasten the chain to the log—the first when the oxen were hitched to the log and the other when it had been drawn to the log pile—and two roller men, whose duty it was after the logs had been drawn to the pile and unfastened by the chain man, to roll the logs by means of hand-spikes and cant-hooks or peavys, on to the pile. The ten-acre slash was divided into twelve equal parts by the owner, John Beaumont, and this he did by outlining with stakes driven into the earth the portion each gang was to log.

There was always great rivalry at these logging bees. To be accounted the champion ox-team gang was looked upon as a great honour. Of these ox-team gangs, that of Stephen Neubecker and of Jack Haag were usually the champions of the settlement. The day of John Beaumont's logging bee, besides those mentioned, Jack Eckford, Moses Stewart, John Bacon, John Lamont, John Brown, Johnston Smith, Bert Godfrey, Dick Everett and Ed. Boulton captained the different ox-teams.

The work went merrily on as the day progressed and the log piles grew apace. The day was bright and clear and the ground fairly dry. Cries of " Whoa! Haw Buck! Gee Bright!" resounded through the " slash " as the drivers speeded up their oxen to greater endeavour in the contest. John and Guy Beaumont circulated amongst the piles with pails of water and a jug of whisky to quench the thirst of any of the workers.

Where the logs lay sparse some of the contestants had little more than an acre to clear, and where they lay thick, somewhat less than that amount.

At noon the men and teams knocked off work for dinner and a rest of a couple of hours, while the oxen were feeding.

Such gatherings of men entailed much labour for the housewife. A cauldron of potatoes was boiled, venison and wild duck in plenty boiled and roasted, bread, butter, and maple syrup and pastry galore; for these new settlers of the wild had voracious appetites. Tables were erected outside the backwoods home, with rough benches stretching along their sides. A boiler of tea, and another of coffee were kept simmering on the stove.

For waiters, Mrs. Beaumont in this emergency called upon some of her neighbours—matrons and maids—from some of the surrounding homesteads, and they generously answered the call.

Alice and Mary Beaumont had their own coterie of girl-friends—Lena and Katie Neubecker; Margaret and Mary Stewart; Fanny Lamont and Bernice Boulton. These young ladies were kept busy supplying the needs of the diners.

About two o'clock the ox-gangs again resumed the logging. It was obvious that Jack Haag drove his oxen with greater energy—amidst yells and curses—than in the forenoon. He also made more frequent application to the whisky jug, and after each application made greater use of his ox-goad in urging his team to greater efforts in order, evidently, to finish his piles first.

Amongst Jack Haag's gang was a chainman, a Frenchman named Mose Larue. He was small of stature but very active, wiry, and with dark hair, eyes and beard. As he saw the results of Neubecker's gang in clearing up their part of the slash he said to Haag:

"Ha! Misteer Jack. Dat feller Steve he beat you!" and he leered into Haag's face.

Haag scowled and redoubled his efforts with the ox-goad.

"For why you not move de stake?" again cried the Frenchman.

" By G---d! I didn't think of that! You're small, Mose, and they can't see you behind the piles. Go over and shift those three stakes in thirty feet on our ground!" called Haag.

" Par dieu! Me! I not was care! But he see me dere was fight!" replied the Frenchman.

" There won't be any fight and they won't see you!" said Haag—" Go ahead."

Larue slipped off and hidden by neighbouring log piles, lifted the line of stakes dividing Haag's allotment from that of Neubecker's and drove them into the ground again fully 30 feet into Haag's lot, thus decreasing the latter's logging " stretch," while it increased that of Neubecker.

The result was that about 4 o'clock Haag's oxen broke one of the bows of their ox-yoke and Guy Beaumont had to hasten away to their log barn and secure another yoke. This accident entailed a delay of about half an hour in the work on Jack Haag's allotment and was put in by the latter in cursing and damning, while he marched up and down casting ugly glances at the neighbouring allotment, that of Stephen Neubecker, whose clearing and piles were nearing completion.

On securing the new yoke from Guy Beaumont, Haag worked with the frenzy of an insane man and drank greater quantities of liquor. Shortly after five o'clock, Stephen Neubecker's gang finished their complement of logging and the two roller men and chainman ascended a large pile, took off their hats and cheered as being the Champions of the Field!

Working desperately, Haag and his gang finished about half an hour later being the second crew to finish. and not long afterwards the different gangs completed their labour.

The men then adjourned to the house, where the cattle were fed and supper partaken of by the loggers. Good-fellowship and jollity pervaded the crowd. Haag alone seemed gloomy, self-contained and ugly and continued his drinking.

After supper, on Stephen Neubecker rising from the bench to get a drink of water, Haag put out his foot and tripped him, and Steve would have had a nasty fall had not George Gordon grabbed his arm.

Recovering himself, Steve turned and said:

"Jack! If that was a joke don't do it again! It's a kind of joke I don't like!" Haag turned to the table where a glass almost filled with whisky and water stood, grabbed it up and flung the contents into Neubecker's face, with the remark "Take that, you long b - - - - r! There's another joke for you!"

Instantly Neubecker was upon him and grasped Haag by the throat. Haag grasped Steve about the waist and rising from his bench—which with some of the table contents, he overturned in the process—attempted to down Steve by "tripping." Instantly uproar reigned about the tables. The screaming of women, wringing of hands, overturning of benches, and the rush and cries of excited men as they made at the two com-batants to separate them, made a veritable pan-demonium.

But John Beaumont elbowed his way through the crowd and placing a hand on the shoulders of each man cried:

"Stop it Haag! Stop it Neubecker! You are my guests at table, and neighbours, and you shall not fight upon my land. Let go, Jack! Steve, I command you to release your hold!"

Reluctantly Haag released his grasp and glowering

at Neubecker, muttered " Another time ! Another day will serve ! "

" Jack Haag, you are no man ! " exclaimed Steve. " I have given you no cause for ill will or enmity. I have offered you my hand in friendship and you have refused it. If you still wish to be my enemy, then have it so ! "

Haag turned without a word and walked off to the stables where, unloosing his ox-team, he made his way homewards.

" Oh ! That drunken Jack Haag has spoiled our evening ! " cried Margaret Stewart. " Yes ! and all because he was jealous at being defeated by Stephen Neubecker at the logging ! " declared pretty Fanny Lamont.

" What a beast he is when he drinks whisky ! " declared Bernice Boulton.

" And Jack isn't so bad when he's sober ! Is he Alice ? " cried teasing Katie Neubecker.

" Oh ! Don't ask me ! I'm disgusted with him after to-night's exhibition ! I never want to see him again ! " and pretty Alice Beaumont, with a spot of red in either cheek, tossed her head in disdain.

Preparations were then made for a dance in the house. The kitchen cleared of furniture—a fiddle produced. One of the " chain-men " tuned up and presently the " row " was forgotten as the young people became absorbed in the pleasures of the dance.

At midnight all sought their homes, but the pleasures of the evening had been marred by the row. All condemned Jack Haag's rowdiness but many put it down to the liquor he had consumed. We shall see in a later chapter that it went deeper than this.

CHAPTER XIX.

THE RAISING.

THE Beaumonts felt very much the want of a suitable barn and stabling for the animals on their premises during the coming winter, the previous winter having been rather severe and with an unusual amount of snow. The log stable, erected during the first summer in the Bush, was poorly constructed and entirely inadequate in size. The fodder had to be placed outside in stacks subject to the inclemency of the elements, besides which wind and snow blew in between the chinks of the structure, and oftentimes they found their animals covered with a coating of snow on a winter's morning.

Therefore the second winter after their settlement in the Bush, John Beaumont decided to build a large log barn, comprising threshing floor and mows for grain and fodder, a granary and stabling for the animals—oxen and cattle—horses having not yet penetrated to that part of Brant.

This he proposed doing by outlining in a suitable location a quadrangle 28 ft. wide and 56 ft. long. This allowed a 16 ft. × 28 ft. threshing floor and two 20 ft. × 28 ft. mows. This, with a side wall height of 14 ft., would give space sufficient for all the crop he could raise on his land for a number of years to come. One end of the building—the eastern—was to be excavated, in the earth, to a depth of 2 ft. Here was to be the stables for the cattle, and overhead the granary.

That winter, therefore, timbers of elm and maple and pine were cut the necessary lengths, hewed and dressed and hauled by means of the oxen to the barn site. Cedar logs were sawn in suitable lengths and shingles split from these blocks were made, and where necessary smoothed off with draw shave.

By spring, all the timbers were ready, but the raising was postponed until seeding had been completed. Accordingly in June when all spring work had been

RAISING LOG BARN.

completed, it was decided to hold the raising. Therefore, on a June day, John Beaumont set out on foot and in the course of two or three days had invited all his neighbours in that part of the township to the Raising on the 25th.

On that day fully 75 men arrived at the Homestead, being almost all the settlers in the western part of Brant Township. Two captains were named, by general acclaim—Pat Godfrey and Jack Everett, and by these sides were chosen. Pike poles (and some lacking these brought poles with a wide crotch on end formed by two projecting limbs), cant-hooks and peaveys, were also brought by the men. Everything was ready by 2 p.m., and then each side began its work.

One company, selecting the north side and west end, while the other company attended to the south side and the east end. Pat Godfrey captained the former, while Jack Everett captained the latter. Four corner men were then selected, two for each side. They were George Gordon and Jack Haag for the north side and Dick Boulton and Johnston Smith for the southern. These corner men had to be expert axemen, sharp of eye, agile, surefooted, as their precarious footing required. Their duty was to attend to the proper laying of the corner logs.

Standing upon the rapidly rising walls and hewing with the axe to make the dove-tailing of the logs fit accurately, so as to leave as little space as possible between logs and so require less " chinking," was the work of these corner men.

The work went merrily on. For the first few rounds of logs that went on the building they were lifted bodily by the men on to the end logs, but as the walls rose higher, skids and pike poles were brought into use to bring the logs into place. The side walls of 20 ft.—on each side of the threshing floor—and the end walls of 28 ft. were light work for the many men.

It was only when the walls rose to 13 ft. in height— the height of the threshing floor doorway—that the 56 ft. logs running the entire length of the building took the united strength of every man on each side with a " Yo— heave—ho! " " Now! " " Yo heave! " " Keep her going boys! " " Shove her home! " until finally " she " landed on the top of the cross walls where the " corner men " quickly settled " her " into place.

Finally, the 14 ft. was attained or raised—the allotted height of the side walls, and the plate beams were put in place. These latter were notched to receive the rafters. The plates were laid simultaneously by either side, neither having an advantage over the other. The corner men then bored holes through the ends of the plates and underlying logs by means of augers and then drove in wooden pins, by means of commanders or beetles, to make all secure.

The corner men then ran around the plates and cross walls to see that all logs fitted and were secure and where necessary a few more blows were applied to the plates.

The men below were at this time resting by the walls, waiting for the call of the corner men for rafters.

Stephen Neubecker was near one end of the building, chatting with Jim Bacon, when suddenly a heavy commander falling from the plate beam above, accompanied by a shout, struck him a glancing blow upon the head and stretched him senseless upon the ground.

An awed silence followed this mishap. The men rushed towards the prostrate body, thinking Steve dead.

" It was Jack Haag's commander !" cried George Stewart from the plate above.

" Yes, it was my commander but it slipped from my hand !" declared Haag, " it was an accident !"

" Are you sure it slipped, Haag?" asked George Stewart.

" It did slip !" said Haag and began walking away upon the top logs to the other side of the barn.

Neubecker's body was picked up and carried under the shade of some trees near-by, where it was laid upon its back, while the men opened the shirt to give air. Steve did not breathe nor could a pulse be felt—in fact he gave no signs of life !

John Eckford told them to bring cold water and towels and bathe his head. This they did and presently Jim Bacon knelt down and placed his ear to Steve's left breast.

"His heart is beating! He's not dead, boys! Move his arms up and down and start him breathing!" he declared.

This was done and shortly Steve making a few irregular inspirations, began breathing.

In the meantime, the raising had come to a standstill. Men gathered in groups discussing the occurrence, and some, remembering the affair of the Logging Bee, did not hesitate to declare that a deliberate attempt at murder had been made by Haag. One or two declared they would not work longer at the raising if Haag remained; that he was a dangerous man; that he might drop another commander upon anyone whom he disliked; at any rate if Haag remained to finish the barn he should come down from off the plate.

But wiser counsels prevailed. Some of the older men pointed out it would not do to show open distrust and suspicion of Haag—that the fall of the commander might have been an accident, and all the more reason to regard it as such now that Neubecker was recovering.

Steve presently sat up and began rubbing his head, but a dizzy spell compelled him to lie down again, when he began vomiting, but by evening he had recovered sufficiently to be on his feet and about but with his head bandaged with a wet towel.

After Steve's vomiting spell was over, the men returned to the building and the rafters were quickly put in place and the job was completed.

As it was still early in the afternoon, being not yet 5 o'clock, the men, as was usual at such raisings, engaged in sports before supper.

These consisted of first a standing broad jump, then a running broad jump, then a standing and a running hop, step and jump; then high jump and finally the vaulting with a pole. In all these exercises Guy Beaumont and George Stewart excelled.

Supper was then called and the men sat down on benches to a bounteous repast, spread on long tables placed near the Log house. The tables were covered with roast beef, venison, wild duck, mashed potatoes and turnips; pies and cakes and doughnuts, butter, maple syrup, molasses and maple sugar galore, while a bevy of young girls and matrons filled cups of steaming coffee and tea for the diners.

Supper over, pipes were lit and reminiscences began; the prospects of the crop; the prices of wheat at Goderich and Penetangore; the prospects of gravel roads, &c. &c.

CHAPTER XX.

The Indian Camp.

INDIANS from the Mouth (Southampton) were frequent travellers on the river passing up and down, on their hunting trips, in their birch bark canoes. Amongst these were two Indian families, John Kubassey and Peter Niwash, with their squaws, who most frequently called at the Beaumont homestead. In John Kubassey's family was a young squaw named Manashay, with coal black eyes and raven hair, sprightly as a young fawn and of a friendly disposition. She and Alice Beaumont quickly became bosom friends. It was very entertaining to listen to Manashay's broken English. She gave Alice the name of the " Wild Rose " due no doubt to her high colour. She also taught Alice the Indian names of many articles and taught her some Chippeway words, to which Alice responded by teaching the Indian girl better English.

One morning on landing from the canoe with her father and mother at the Beaumont homestead, she ran towards the home and seeing Alice outside cried—

" Bosho ! Ikwe !" (Good-day, lady !).

" Good day ! Good day !" replied Alice, "why, Manashay, how are you ! It's so long since you visited me ! Come on into the house !"

" Noss manj ain !" (my father is unwell) said Manashay. " Si ki Scudawaboo ?" (Have you whisky ?)

Alice shook her head. " Say it in English, Manashay, I don't understand you !" replied Alice.

" My fader, he very sick in canoe. Have you fire water?" said the Indian girl.

" I will see!" replied the girl and ran into the house, from which she presently emerged with a glass of hot toddy, which she gave the Indian girl and accompanied her to the water's edge, where the canoe lay— Kubassey's squaw and Kubassey himself were in the canoe—the latter doubled up in pain and lying in the bottom.

" Anin eji-aiaian Nosse!" (How art thou, father?) cried Manashay.

" Nind akoo sa!" (I am sick) said Kubassey.—" Anin enapineian?" (What is thy sickness?).—" Niad akooh-kade!" (I have belly-ache).—" Minikwe Kijate Scuda-waboo!" (Drink the hot whisky). And Manashay handed him the glass of steaming toddy. This Kubassey did, and the glow of the liquor soon pervaded his body, so that presently he stood up, jumped on the shore and began helping his squaw to build a fire, expressing himself as feeling better.

On re-embarking that evening for their home, the Indians invited the Beaumont family to visit the Indian camp at the Mouth. This the Beaumonts promised to do, but urgent matters on the farm prevented for some time. But one bright spring day, when the woods had put on their fairest coat of green and wild flowers were springing up in every glade, Alice said to her mother—

" Mother, now would be a good time to pay our visit to the Indian camp at the Mouth. I would like to see Manashay and the other squaws and John Kubassey's little papoose! Do let us go!"

" We will have to see father about it first!" replied the mother. " He is very busy with the spring work and I don't think he will go!"

"Oh! We will get some of the neighbours to go along. The Neubeckers, Gordons, Lamonts, Stewarts and Everetts will be glad to go along. We can go in canoes and return the same day!" said Alice. "Well! We'll see!" said the mother.

The matter was brought up again that day at the dinner table and the boys—Guy, Alex and Jack—were enthusiastically in its favour as was also Miss Mary.

"Oh! Won't that be fine!" Mary declared. "Now daddy you mustn't say no! We haven't had a holiday this year, and you must give us this one!" And the girl, who was her father's favourite, slipped her arms around her father's neck and gave him a hug and a kiss. "Say yes, Daddy!"

"Well! It must be properly arranged and a number of you go together!" said the father.

"You mustn't go down there all alone amongst all those Indians! Who is going along?" enquired John Beaumont.

"There will be plenty to go along, have the sail and see the sights!" said Guy. "I will see the young men along the river and arrange the outing. We can go down in canoes and be at the Mouth in three hours!" said Guy.

These birch bark canoes were made by the Indians and were about 20 ft. in length and about 3 ft. wide at their widest part; framework—gunwales and ribs—of cedar, over which was stretched sheets of birch bark, sewn together with the fine fibre of tamarac roots and the seams covered with hot pitch; split cedar was placed in the bottom for a floor. The whole structure was so light that one man could carry it with ease, and it was capable of carrying four or five people or eight or nine hundredweight of baggage. A good canoe, well built would last five or six years. In rowing the canoe, two men are required. One in the bow to row and another in the stern to steer. In rowing the canoe, the oarsman sits on his knees and, grasping the oar with one hand near the blade, and the other at the end of the handle, without touching the gunwale of the frail bark pushes the water away from him with the blade of the oar.

A few days after this Guy had arranged all the preliminaries in extending invitations to participate in the proposed river picnic, and it was decided to make the trip on the following Wednesday.

The river was high, being in flood and with considerable current, and it was estimated the canoes would easily make the trip to the Mouth in three hours. To return would of course require longer.

On the Sunday evening before the day set for departure, Stephen Neubecker called at Beaumont's. "Well Stephen, are you 'all set' for Wednesday morning?" cried Alice, looking roguishly in Stephen's face. "Yes! But I've come to ask you, Alice, to go along with me in my canoe?" and Stephen turned a supplicating face to the girl.

"Oh! I'm going with our boys, in our own canoe!" replied Alice. "Your arrangement wouldn't do at all, Stephen!" she cried, "it would cause jealousy, and jealousy, you know, Stephen, is a bad thing!" and the girl laughed heartily.

"Please go with me, Alice! I've been counting on it! Other girls will be going with fellows in their canoes and why can't you go along with me?" and poor Stephen put on a most lugubrious countenance.

"Well, I'll tell you what I'll do, Stephen! If your sister Lena accompanies us in the canoe I'll go along with you!" and Alice cast a side-glance at Stephen.

" Oh ! Lena don't want to go with me ! Why do you want her?" replied Steve.

" Well ! It's Lena or nothing ! If you want me, bring her along !" said Alice with decision.

It was finally so arranged. The next Wednesday morning Steve was at Beaumont's landing bright and early with his canoe and accompanied by his sister Lena, and with a generous supply of lunches stowed aboard.

Presently a whoop from down the river drew attention to a canoe making rapidly for the landing. It contained George and Mary Gordon. They quickly landed, making fast their canoe. " Hallo Steve ! How goes it ? What are you doing here?" cried George. " I thought you'd be away down river by now !"

" No ! I came up for my passenger, Miss Alice !" replied Steve.

" Miss Alice ? Why I expected to take her along with us !" exclaimed George.

" Too late ! You can't get her ! She's mine !" laughingly replied Steve.

Alice now came tripping down to the landing, accompanied by her brothers, these latter laden with packages of picnic lunches which had been put up for them by their mother. Greeting her friends, Alice took her place in Steve's canoe with Steve at the bow and Lena at the stern. Under the vigorous strokes of the paddlers, and Stephen was no tyro at the business, the birch canoe passed rapidly down the swollen river, closely followed by Beaumont's canoe, controlled by Guy and Jack and Mary Gordon aboard, and George Gordon in his canoe with Mary and Alex Beaumont, following. Passing rapidly down the river, they reached their neighbours to the west, when out from Haag's landing

shot a canoe with Jack Haag and Jim and George Weir.
These exchanged greetings with the canoes sailing by
and then dropped in behind—the others passing onwards. At the different homesteads, down river, other
canoes joined the flotilla. Archie Stewart and his two
sisters—Mary and Margaret—Dick Everett, Ed.
Boulton, Pat Godfrey and John Brown, each craft laden
with some members of its owners' family, aboard.

By nine o'clock on the forenoon they had reached the
junction of the Yokissippi with the Saugeen and passed
Simon Orchard's Settlement at that place, waving to a
group of people watching the flotilla sail by. Here the
river broadened out and they entered the wide reaches
of the stream in Saugeen Township and drove rapidly
away to the northwards, following which came a wide
sweep to the north-east, after which came a wide circle to
the west and the river headed westwards into the lake.

By eleven o'clock they had reached the lake and
landed on the south shore of the Mouth close to the
Indian village and with the green waters of Lake Huron
booming on the beach to the westwards.

From far out on the horizon the green waves of Mer
Douce, their tops crested white with foam, came rolling
in, to break in thunder on the sandy and rock-strewn
shore in clouds of spume.

The Argonauts gathered in a group, gazing seaward,
spell-bound by the sight. To the west, south and north
and to the distant horizon—far as sight could see—the
broad expanse showed one mass of rolling waves—with
here and there a lather of white—where a wave larger
than its fellows broke in a smother of foam. No boat,
no canoe; not a sail of any kind was to be seen upon its
rolling surface. Both shore lines to the south and to
the north presented an unbroken line of dark forest,

reaching down to the beach and stretching away to the horizon on either hand.

Gazing to satiety, the party now turned to survey the landward side of the Mouth.

Saugeen, or the Mouth, as it was often called in the early days (later changed to Southampton), was at the time of which we write a small place of 200 to 300 people with three taverns, the Crown Lands Office and a number of log houses. The Crown Lands Agent at that time was Alex McNab, whose house and office was a small log·building 16 × 18 ft. in size.

The taverns were built of logs, as were most of the other buildings of the Settlement. Alex Belcher's tavern was built in 1854. The first settlers were Captain John Spence and Captain Wm. Kennedy, old Hudson Bay employees, who had located at the Mouth about 1848 for fur trading with the Indians.

The building of Spence and Kennedy was erected on the tongue of land to the north of the mouth of the river, between it and the lake, while across the Mouth and on its southern shore were 25 to 30 wigwams—the Indian village—the homes of the Sauking or Saugeen Band of Chippeway Indians.

The party now drew up their canoes upon the beach and the hampers of lunches were unloaded; a camp fire was built; water boiled and tea made and presently the party sat down to a bounteous lunch, and with appetites whetted by the Lake breeze, ample justice was speedily done to it. Jollity and good fellowship reigned.

After a satisfying meal, the party broke up into two's and three's to visit the Indian Camp. Stephen and Alice Beaumont, George Gordon and Mary Beaumont; Guy Lamont and Mary Gordon, George Weir and Mary Stewart, invaded the tepees. These tepees or wigwams were built of poles. Twenty or thirty poles 15 to 18 ft. long were arranged vertically so that they all touched each other at the top but with their bases so arranged circularly as to enclose a space of ground 12-15 ft. in diameter.

These poles had birch and elm bark spread over them externally. A fire made in the centre of the enclosed ground plot found a smoke vent through the opening at the top.

On the inside of the wigwam and upon the ground around its walls, branches and rushes were strewn, upon which bear and deer skins were laid, for couches and seats for the inmates. Depending from the poles, immediately above the fire in the wigwam, and in the smoke, jerked meat was hung. This jerking consisted of cutting bear and deer meat into very thin slices, and spread upon a grid-iron 3 feet from the ground and covered with switches, on which the meat was placed and a fire kindled below it and kept up until there was no longer any moisture in the meat. The meat thus became dry as a piece of wood. This put up in packages of 30 or 40 pieces and rolled in pieces of bark and then hung in the wigwams, would keep for a very long time, without spoiling.

When desired for food it was pounded between two stones and cooked in water with Indian corn.

Having entered the tepees, the picnic party found many old Indian acquaintances of the river, amongst them Peter Niwash, John Kubassey and his daughter Manashay—and squaws, John Madawayosh. " Bosho ! Nitchi !'' exclaimed Peter Niwash, coming forward to meet Stephen Neubecker and Alice Beaumont, who were in the forefront of the party and shaking hands with them. "Bosho! Bosho! Peter!" cried Alice, anxious to air her Chippeway.

John Kubassey now approached the group and Alice again cried "Bosho! John! Bosho!"

"Bosho! Nin Nimo Aia!" (I am well) replied the

INDIAN GIRL.

Indian. "Koss, Kya Aia?" (Is thy father and mother well?)

"Nix versteh John!" laughingly replied Alice, shaking her head. "I guess we'd better stick to English, if we wish to understand each other! I'm hardly far enough advanced to hold a conversation in Chippeway. Perhaps some day with Manashay's help I may!"

" He say " Your fader and moder well?" broke in
Peter Niwash.

" Oh! Yes John! They are fine, but they didn't
come along with us. We are all young people on this
trip! We've come on a picnic! But where is Manashay?" cried Alice. " I want to see her; and Peter,
where is your little papoose Panginini? I must
see him!"

" Papoose and squaw gone up river fish!" said
Peter, " come back bye and bye!" and he waved his
hand up the river.

Just then Manashay, the young Indian girl, emerged
from a neighbouring wigwam and warmly welcomed
Alice. She wore a skirt of dressed deer skin very soft
to the touch and embroidered at the bottom and waist
with coloured beads; leggings and moccasins of the same
material, ornamented on the sides and top with glass
beads and varied coloured porcupine quills. A shawl
enveloped her shoulders; her raven black hair was
dressed closely to her head and extended down her back
in two plaits. Her expression was one of great vivacity
and was pleasing. A round face, rather broad nose and
brown eyes and pearl-white teeth completed a charming
forest personality. " The ' Wild Rose ' come to visit
Indian girl?" she exclaimed on shaking hands, " and
with her man!" looking at Steve.

" No! Oh no!" cried Alice blushing a bright red,
" we are a party on a picnic trip and Steve and I just
happened to come together " (Stephen's face fell!)
" Won't you show us your camp, Manashay?"

The Indian girl conducted them to her wigwam,
which on raising a flap of birch bark they entered—a
small fire burned in a circle of perhaps 20 ft. in diameter;
around the base of the walls were laid cedar and

hemlock branches upon which were laid bearskins, while
from the poles depended the bundles of jerked meat as
in the wigwams they had already inspected. An old
Indian woman—not Manashay's mother—was attend-
ing to the fire over which a pot, giving off the aroma
of some savoury stew, was steaming. "The 'Wild
Rose' and her man have some soup?" inquired
Manashay.

Alice reddened but nodded assent. She wished to
thoroughly explore everything in the Indian camp—
the victuals as well as the wigwams. Taking their
seats upon the bear skins the Indian girl procured a
couple of bowls and dipping them into the pot of stew
handed one to each of the visitors. Spoons being an
unknown luxury at the Indian camp at that time, Alice
and Steve were forced to sip the broth from the bowls
with their lips.

The stew was composed of pounded corn mixed with
water and called sagamite and into which pieces of jerked
deer meat—also after being pounded with stone—had
been added. It really formed a very good and nourish-
ing stew.

On going out into the open—for the smell of the
wigwam was rather strong for the white girl—they
found the other members of the party busily engaged
visiting the other wigwams.

Alice again expressed a wish to see Peter's little
papoose before returning home and upon the Indian
girl learning this, she offered to conduct them up river
where her sister—Peter's wife—was likely to be engaged
in fishing and most likely to be found. The two whites
and the Indian girl therefore passed into the woods,
following an Indian trail up river.

After proceeding in this manner for half a mile, the
trail divided into two. Of these, one trail approached

the river and the other struck off more deeply into the woods and more at right angles from the stream. Manashay took the former or left-hand trail and at an angle of the path came suddenly upon Peter's papoose, strapped to a papoose frame or cradle, and the latter swinging from the branch of a tree, but within a few feet of the ground.

With a cry of delight, Alice sprang forward to the child and lifting him out of his cradle took him in her arms and sat down.

The Indian boy was probably a year old, with round chubby face and rolling black eyes and raven black hair. He did not cry, evidently having no fear of his visitor, only rolling his black eyes from Alice to Steve in childish wonder. The Indian girl stood by, a look of amusement visible on her keen face—no doubt she ascribed the delight of Alice, on seeing the papoose, to its true cause—the maternal instinct. Presently she said she would seek out her sister and bring her to the " white squaw " and disappeared up the trail.

" Oh ! look, Stephen ! Isn't this just a perfectly cute baby !" cried Alice. " Did you ever see anything like it ? What heavenly eyes and see how he rolls them and watches every movement ! I just think he's too cute for anything ! I am going to ask Peter for him ! I'd love to take him home and keep him !" declared the delighted girl.

" Oh, that would never do, Alice ! Think ! Peter and his squaw would never consent nor would your parents ! Besides, what would a young lady want with an Indian baby ?" cried Stephen.

" See ! He is taking to me already !" exclaimed the girl as the Indian child fastened his black eyes upon a gold brooch which she wore in her dress at the throat, and at the same time endeavoured to grasp it with his little fingers. "Isn't he a dear!" exclaimed the delighted girl, and gave the child a hug.

"Alice, I want to ask you something," said Stephen at this juncture. "I have often wanted to speak of it but never had the opportunity before! Will you marry me, Alice?"

"Oh, Stephen! Now you've spoiled my outing! Why do you talk that way? Can't you be content for us just to be friends? I esteem and respect you, Stephen, but what you ask can never be!" exclaimed the girl. "Surely there is someone who would be a greater help and comfort to you than I could ever be!"

"Then there is someone else?" cried poor Stephen.

"You have no right to say that!" exclaimed the girl "I never encouraged you in any way. I hope we will always be friends, Stephen. It can never be otherwise!"

"Oh! Alice! Do not say no! Take time—as long as you like—to consider" and in his eagerness he grasped Alice's hand with an imploring look upon his face.

At this instant a voice broke on their ears—the bushes parted and Jack Haag emerged on to the trail.

"Ho! Ho! A love scene! I thought something of the kind was afoot, when I saw both of you take the trail into the woods!" cried Haag.

Alice jerked her hand away from Stephen's grasp and arose holding the Indian child in her arms.

"I might have known you'd play the sneak and spy, Jack Haag. It's your nature! But it's not a love scene. Stephen Neubecker is my friend and will always remain so! I'm sure he will never spy on my movements as you have done!" cried the outraged girl.

A noise on the trail now betokened the arrival of

Manashay and her sister, who now appeared. Peter's wife bore a long string of fish, strung on to a birch branch. The Indian woman went up to Alice, greeted her quietly and taking the child and putting him again in his cradle swung the latter to her back and passing the cradle straps around her shoulders, said—

"Come, we go back to camp!" struck into the trail followed by the girls—Indian and white—with Stephen Neubecker bringing up the rear and leaving Jack Haag standing in gloomy silence upon the trail behind them.

Mid-afternoon had now arrived and on the picnic party gathering together it was decided it would soon be time to begin the homeward journey. The canoes would not have the benefit of the current, as they had in coming down the river, but would have to battle against it. For this reason an early start was deemed advisable.

Just then Peter Niwash approached them and apprised them the band wished to honor them—before their return—with a feast. Their paleface friends did not often visit them at the Mouth, while many of their people had experienced the hospitality of the whites at their different homesteads along the river, on the frequent hunting trips of the aborigines.

Of course, the invitation was accepted. It would not do to affront their hosts by refusing to partake of a feast, more especially as the novelty of an Indian feast appealed to many of the young people.

Presently all the male Indians arranged themselves, sitting upon the ground, in a large circle of about 50 yards in diameter, inviting their white guests to sit amongst them in the circle. This circle was just in front of the Indian camp. Upon this being done, the squaws and young Indian women going around outside the circle passed around from hand to hand, large pieces of bark upon which slices of boiled deer meat (venison), smoking hot, had been piled. This was passed from hand to hand, each person helping himself or herself from the natural platter—the bark—with the fingers. The next course was pieces of bark with boiled Lake trout, sliced—upon them. Then came roast bear steak and finally cakes of pounded Indian corn—hot from the ashes of the fires where they had baked.

These viands the whites partook of freely—the men especially praising the bill of fare highly. Some of the girls, however, were a little shy of the meats, but partook freely of the fish and corn cakes. " I don't know!" said pretty Mary Stewart. " Alice! This may be boiled dog for all I know! What do you think? I tasted it but won't eat it!"

" For shame! Mary! It is good deer meat!" replied Alice. " You will offend our hosts if they hear you!"

The feast over, the canoes were carried down to the water and, bidding adieu to their Indian friends, the party embarked for their homes and resumed the homeward journey, which they reached by midnight after a weary pull up stream, but with everybody well pleased with the outing—except Alice and Stephen.

CHAPTER XXI.

The Pow Wow.

Upon one of their many canoe trips up and down the river, in the spring of that year, when on their hunting expeditions, John Kubassey and Peter Niwash, Indians from the Mouth, had persuaded them to hold a pow wow at Beaumont's homestead on the 24th of the following May—the Queen's Birthday. The Queen's Birthday was the first chief holiday of the summer and was always generally observed, not only in the new, but in the older parts of the Province of Upper Canada. It was anticipated that the event would be well attended.

Guy estimated this Indian performance would attract a record crowd, bringing together all or almost all of the settlers in the western part of the township and probably some from the adjoining parts of the neighbouring townships of Greenock and Elderslie.

Pow wows were a rare event in that part of the Province. They were only held to celebrate some unusual occurrence in the affairs of the Indian tribes— the signing of a treaty of peace—or the transfer of a section of their territory to the Whites. Also in honour of a visit from the Lieut.-Governor or Governor-General.

The pow wow was a dance and feast—a public and noisy celebration always preceding some important action—an expedition, a hunt, a treaty, or in honour of some prominent personage.

Accordingly, early on the morning of the 24th of May, a flotilla of canoes from the Mouth were seen approaching the homestead from down river. They comprised some dozen birch bark canoes, loaded with Indians—bucks and squaws—the papooses being left at home in charge of some of the older squaws at the Mouth.

The bucks were gaudily dressed in tunics of tanned deer hide, with a string of bears' claws around the neck and with leggings and moccasins also of dressed deer hide. On their heads they wore a headdress made of eagle feathers, which turned aloft giving them a very martial appearance. The head was shaved except a tuft of hair growing from the crown—the scalp lock—following the custom of their nation. Some had painted their faces for the pow wow. Streaks of red and green, yellow and black paint had been applied round the eyes and mouth and down their cheeks giving them a truly devilish appearance. A belt around the waist holding a tomahawk completed the costume.

The squaws wore skirts of dressed doe skin, these and the moccasins being of softer leather than the clothing of the bucks, and wore bright, gaudy shawls draping from the shoulders, with their black hair dressed tightly to the head and hanging down the back in pleats.

The flotilla drew in to the landing at Beaumont's—where a considerable crowd of whites had already gathered—and disembarked. They numbered between 50 and 60 people—the great majority being males Salutations were exchanged with the whites. Many of Beaumont's acquaintances were amongst the Indians—Chief Alex Madwayosh, Tom and John Wahbuddick;

Charley Keeshick, John Kadugehkivan; the Indian girl Manashay, John Kubassey and Peter Niwash, besides many others and a bevy of Indian girls.

After greetings had been exchanged, the bucks went into the surrounding forest and returned presently laden with birch branches about 2 ft. long. These had been cut off with a sharpened end in order to be more readily shoved into the ground. These branches were then stuck in the ground about a foot apart, and enclosing a circle of about 50 ft. in diameter, leaving an opening— to the west—of about 5 ft. for entrance to the circle and in which no branches were stuck. Hemlock and cedar brush, or branches, were then laid upon the ground for a width of 2 ft. on the inside of this circle, adjacent to the upright branches. These served as seats for the participants of the pow wow.   -

All the settlers along that part of the river had heard of the celebration to be held at Beaumont's. As it was Queen Victoria's Birthday and a general holiday they gathered in crowds to see the pow wow. The Neubeckers; Haags; Stewarts; Boltons; Godfreys; Browns; Bacons; Everetts; Gordons; Johnstons; and many more from that part of the township, all were there. Each family had brought a large basket of provisions, not only for their own lunches but also to treat their Indian friends.

A huge fire had been made in the clearing by the Beaumont boys, over which hung a huge sugar kettle of steaming coffee, while a couple of large tables—made of boards—stood hard by upon which were spread piles of venison sandwiches, together with cakes, doughnuts and elderberry pies, and to which were added the contents of the settlers' baskets.

As the Indians always feast before performing a war dance—Guy Beaumont, who acted as Master of Ceremonies, told Kubassey that the Indians were to seat themselves in a circle and the food would be brought round to them.

Alice and Mary Beaumont, together with several of the other young women of the settlement, went around the circle distributing cups to each Indian while some of the settlers followed with large tins of steaming coffee, while other young women passed around sandwiches, cakes, doughnuts, and pies, etc. This was kept up until the piles upon the tables were considerably diminished.

Satiety at length reached, the Indians brought out the Peace Pipe. This had a red sandstone bowl representing the figure of a man in a sitting posture, to which was attached a long wooden stem with a bone mouthpiece—this latter from the legbone of a wild turkey. The Peace Pipe was stuffed with tobacco and lit. Upon this the Chief, Alex Madwayosh, inhaled the smoke, and emitting a puff to the four cardinal points, east, west, north and south, passed the pipe on to one of his companions. This Indian, emitting also a couple of puffs, passed it on.

In this way it passed around the circle of Indians and then reached the white men. John Beaumont was the first of these to smoke the pipe, and emitting a couple of puffs passed it on to the remainder of the whites present.

Amity, concord and good feeling being thus assured, the Indians arose and slowly passing into the circle of twigs before mentioned, took their places upon the rushes spread around the inside of the circle of birch-twigs—sitting cross-legged on the ground.

In the meantime four young bucks had entered the circle, and placing a drum or tom-tom in the centre thereof, sat down cross-legged around it. This drum was of well-tanned deer hide, stretched very tightly over a circular frame of elm. Around the drum and driven into the ground were 8 thin wands about 2½ ft. in length, their sides wound with narrow cloths or ribbons of blue, white and red, and whose ends hung down in a festoon from the top of the wands. These wands surrounded the drum in pairs, two on the east side; two on the west side; two on the north and two on the south. The wands were driven into the earth about 3 inches apart. The skill of the buck was estimated by not only keeping time to the tune but by bringing down his drum stick exactly between the two upright wands before him on the edge of the drum.

The drum sticks were about 1½ feet long, their ends padded with hair and covered with buck skin, the handle part of the implement being about three-quarters of an inch in thickness and made of elm.

Upon the four young bucks taking their places about the drum, about a dozen young squaws entered the circle and arranging themselves around the bucks and in an outer circle also squatted on the ground, their shawls drawn over their heads and draping off their shoulders, and so formed the orchestra of this forest entertainment; and the séance began.

Each buck brought his drumstick down—in time with the others—between two of the gaudily bedecked uprights before him and produced a deep boom which could be heard at long distances.

The measure was at first slow and accompanied by a low explosive " Hi-yah " from the bucks. At the same time the squaws began an eerie wail of low pitch but in perfect time to the accompaniment of the drum. As the music proceeded the tune increased and the actions of the drummers became more excited. The boom of the drum could be heard a couple of miles away.

As the music increased in intensity an Indian—who had previously been sitting cross-legged inside the birch circle—would arise, the body bent forward, the feet raised in measured footsteps to time with the drums, while the arms were held with elbows to the side and forearms and clenched hands directed forwards, and so with the tread of a spring halt horse, a fierce look upon his face and yelling his " Hiyah !" the aborigine circled the enclosure to the beat of the drums. As the spirit moved them others of the sitting Indians sprang to their feet and joined the gesticulating and yelling circle, until finally all had arisen and formed a moving, shouting, circling, frenzied band with glaring eyeballs, scowling faces, moving in unison with each other and to the beat of the drum, and resembled nothing so much as a nightmare of devils engaged in their peculiar orgies.

The whites gazed on this exhibition with awe and, to some of the young white women, awe not unmixed with fear.

The pow wow was kept up for some time, until finally exhausted nature claimed a part and the Indians resumed their seats inside the circle of branches.

The Indians then broke up the pow wow and began making preparations to resume the water journey to the Mouth, but Jack Haag, Dick Everett and a few other young men of the settlement determined to have some fun with their forest friends before they re-embarked.

Jack Haag therefore went up to Charley Keeschick and patting his breast pocket said—

" Charley like a little scudawaboo ?" (whisky). The Indian's face brightened. A glad look came into his face.

"White man got fire water? Give!" and extended his hand.

Jack shook his head and said "Not here! Come into the woods and bring Chief Madwayosh and John Wahbuddick!" saying which he walked into the surrounding forest followed by Charley. Here pulling a flask from his pocket he gave it to the Indian who would have drained the contents without once removing it from his lips had not Jack grabbed the bottle from him.

"Oh, I say, Charley! Have a little style about you! Leave some for the other fellows!" At this, Charley looked at the bottle longingly, licking his lips and said "Good fire water!"

Madwayosh and the Wahbuddicks together with Dick Everett, George Stewart and others now joined the group, and flasks with which some of the young men had come prepared, were produced and given to the Indians. The effect of this was soon seen. The reeling forms of the Indians were seen in all directions.

In the meantime, Alice Beaumont had taken Manashay, the Indian girl, accompanied by a bevy of Indian maids, to the Beaumont homestead to show them the splendours of some quilts she had made. The Indian maids were shy and timid on entering the settlers' dwelling. Mrs. Beaumont endeavoured to put them at ease by furnishing them with cups of hot tea and cake, while Alice exhibited the quilts. On admiring these a great uproar was heard without in the clearing. On rushing to the door, they beheld two parties of about a dozen Indians each, uttering war cries, brandishing clubs and knives and rushing at each other in mortal combat. The combatants reeled from drunkenness while attacking each other, and some of them fell helpless to the earth. Their blows when they did strike were nerveless. Blows were struck which, if the fighters were in their full senses, would have killed or maimed for life, had little effect upon an opponent.

The whites now awoke to the danger which had been created. John Beaumont took charge and some of the older settlers went from Indian to Indian and removed any whisky flasks which were to be found and called out in a loud voice that any young white man found guilty of giving liquor to an Indian would be prosecuted to the full extent of the law.

At that time—in fact both before and since—giving liquor to an Indian was a penitentiary offence.

Gradually order was resumed—the drunken Indians were loaded into their canoes by their sober friends and passed down river to their home. The bulk of the visitors remained for an outdoor supper in the glade, given them by the Beaumonts, and such was the appetites of the aborigines that not a scrap of food of any kind was left after the meal was finished. Adieus were then made and the children of the forest departed for their homes at the Mouth, leaving the white settlers with their first experience of a pow wow!

CHAPTER XXII.

MAKING MAPLE SUGAR.

ABOUT the middle of March, when the sun was daily mounting higher in the heavens and the snow had begun to disappear and with clear cold frosty nights, Mrs. Beaumont said at the breakfast table one morning, "Sap will soon begin to run! Alex, you and Jack go out to the Bush this afternoon and tap a couple of trees so we can tell if it's time to begin our sugar making!"

Accordingly, that afternoon, loaded with a couple of sap pails, wooden spiles, an auger and an axe, the two boys travelled back through their clearing to the woods and tapped some trees. This was done by selecting medium-sized and vigorous looking maple trees and by means of the auger boring a hole into the trunk about three inches in depth and driving into it a perforated wooden spile—made of cedar, and 6 or 8 inches long with a gutter or channel along which the maple sap could run. The day was bright and clear, with a tang to the air, but with no wind. Shortly a few drops of sap began dripping into the pails which had been set upon the ground at the base of the tree and below the spiles. "Sap was running!"

They returned home, reporting "Sap running" and preparations then began to build a sugar camp the next day. Accordingly, the next morning they loaded up the sleigh, with sap buckets, shovels, axes, augers, pails, sugar kettles and barrels for holding the sap; hammers and nails and material, in the shape of boards,

for building the camp. Hitching on the oxen—
"Buck" and "Bright"—to the load, they slowly made
their way back to the Bush.

While Alex cleared the ground of snow for a camp,
Jack began tapping the maple trees; boring the holes;
driving in the spiles and setting the buckets below the
spiles at the base of the tree.

Alex meantime had selected four young trees, being
the corners of a parallelogram six by ten feet, and
boarded up the three sides thereof, viz., north, west and

MAKING MAPLE SUGAR.

east, leaving the fourth or south side open to the fire.
The walls were boarded to a height of six or seven feet.
The roof was covered with sheets of hemlock bark.
The interior held a table, a bench and a bunk for sleep-
ing purposes.

Fronting the open side of the camp, two large logs—
ten feet long—were brought within a couple of feet of
each other and a fire built between them. At each end
of the logs, upright crotched posts were set in the ground

and a long stout elm pole was laid on these crotched posts.

Upon this pole the boiling kettles (usually three) were hung. The barrels were arranged conveniently near the boiling kettles.

A good " run of sap " in the early days was six quarts in two hours, but all depended on the weather. As before said, if the nights were cold, clear and frosty and the days sunny and warm—and not too warm, the " sap run " was most generous. While rain, snow or stormy weather retarded it. If it was a good year and a good "sap run" the barrels were quickly filled and had to be transferred by the foreman from barrel to first boiling kettle, and as this boiled down was transferred to the second boiling kettle, while the first was replenished from the sap barrel. A huge fire was kindled and kept going night and day whilst the " sap run " lasted.

One man was continually cutting fuel and feeding it to the fire. Another periodically gathered the sap from the sap buckets and brought it to the sap barrels.

If the distance was not too great from the farthest trees to the camp fire, that is if the settler was only making sugar on a moderate scale, he gathered his sap in two large pails suspended from a yoke upon his shoulders, and this was sufficient to take care of any ordinary run of sap; but if the distance or the number of trees tapped was too great then an ox hitched to a stone boat upon which was placed a large sap barrel, was used for the gathering; to prevent " slopping over " of the sap a piece of heavy canvas covered the barrel.

The duty of the boiler was to dip sap from barrel to kettle, as this boiled down, to transfer it by means of a dipper to the second boiling kettle, and later thence to

the third—also to scoop out cinders and dead leaves from
the boiling kettles and also to prevent the sap boiling
over.

A piece of fat pork tied to the end of a stick and stuck
into the boiling sap or rubbed around the top of the
boiling fluid where it joined the metal pot prevented the
sap boiling over.

As the sap thickened it was transferred from kettle to
kettle, being dipped from one to the other, until finally
it was reduced to syrup. At this stage, to remove the
ashes, refuse, and debris which had fallen into the sap in
the process of burning, a pint of sweet milk would be
thrown into the sap; this would gather the debris to the
surface when it could be scooped out with the dipper and
thrown away. A fresh egg broken and its contents
thrown into the sap would serve the same purpose as
the milk.

Sap boiling began usually in March and lasted oftentimes until May, if the weather was favorable and the
" run " was great. Some years the sap ran only for a
couple of weeks. This of course would be due to
broken weather, rains, storms, cloudy and windy
weather. And strange to say, weather that was favourable for sap running and sugar making was bad for the
settlers' fall wheat. The hard freezing nights with
warm, sunny, thawing days—ideal weather for sap—
would heave the wheat roots from the soil and destroy
them by frost! Such is farming life!

In sap-boiling 5 pails of sap were usually boiled down
to one pail, which was then transferred to a second
kettle. When the third kettle was boiled down to what
was deemed a proper consistence the process of
" sugaring off " was begun. The boiler was the person to do this. To do so he took a short birch twig,

from twelve to fifteen inches long. The small end was tied on to the main stem so as to make a loop an inch or two in diameter. On this loop being dipped into the boiling sap and held up in the air, upon being blown upon would—if of the proper consistence to form sugar —form a large, shiny, beautiful bubble, sometimes as large as two fists, but which shortly thereafter, due to cooling, collapsed. This was also sometimes done with a silver spoon attached to the end of a stick and a small quantity of syrup removed from the boiling sap. If when blown upon it formed a bubble it indicated "sugaring off." At this stage the boiler required care in handling the fire—too great a heat burned the "make" and spoiled the sugar. When the "bubble" was attained the syrup was of the proper consistency to make sugar. Then dishes, vessels, patty pans, tart tins and what not were brought out, their inside greased and the boiling syrup poured therein, whence arose the many shapes of the maple sugar cakes of the early days.

Some of the settlers adopted the device of having a pipe with a very narrow bore—about the diameter of a straw—connecting the bottom of the sap barrel to the first boiling kettle on the fire. By this means a steady stream of small size was delivered into the boiling sap kettle, the liquid being kept at more even temperature than in the process of dipping from barrel to kettle, and hence no slowing down of the boiling.

Sometimes the sugar was allowed to remain *en masse* in the kettle. When this was desired a rag was wound around the end of a stick well greased with lard and the inside of the kettle on sides and bottom where the boiling sap came in contact with the metal, was well rubbed with the rag. The kettle was then removed from the fire and allowed to cool, when the fluid would settle in a mass of sugar. This, when it had solidified and the kettle was overturned, would fall out in one mass.

To make taffy, the settler, previous to getting the syrup in the third kettle to the consistency of sugar, added snow to the syrup and poured it out on to the snow where it quickly cooled to the consistency of sweetmeat. This was greatly enjoyed by the young folks. Alex Beaumont had a small setter dog called Toby. Toby always accompanied his master on his travels and on this particular night had ranged the woods neighbouring to the sugar-making camp and sitting on his haunches had watched the taffy making. From a spirit of mischief Alex threw him a lump of warm taffy. Toby grabbed it in his mouth, while it was in mid-air and sank his teeth into it, but what was his horror when he found the teeth glued to the lump and unable to open his mouth. A look of surprise mingled with reproach as he glanced at his master and then tumbled in the snow, rolling over and over in an endeavour to loosen the sticky lump from his mouth. All in vain—the only way he could rid himself of the taffy was to allow it to melt in his mouth, which it did in the course of an hour.

To boil sap down into sugar usually required two or three days' continuous boiling and stirring in order that the fluid would not burn. At "sugaring off" times the neighbours often participated.

The night scenes at the sugar camp were often very picturesque. The ruddy light of the huge fires; the boiling cauldrons; the warm earth around the camp from which the snow had been melted by the heat of the huge fires; the dim woods stretching afar; the figures in the firelight formed a strange scene in the silent woods— silent except for the mournful hoot of the horned owl or the distant chatter of a chipmonk.

When the settler was poor and financially unable to buy sap buckets, stout basswood logs were split in two and hollowed out with the axe to form sap-troughs, which were quickly made and served the purpose of sap buckets. To expedite the boiling, fires were kept going day and night. Wood or fuel then was of no consideration. It was worth nothing.

There was wood everywhere—wood galore. The more wood that was burned the more clearing there would be for grain growing. Hence the holocaust went on.

Maple sugar, in the early days of settlement, was plentiful and cheap. A common price for it in those early times was 1½ cents per lb. and was largely used in the backwoods homes throughout the year; as well as being cheaper than the store sugar it was sweeter and healthier.

Muscovado or brown sugar sold in the village stores for $1.50 per lb. and white granulated sugar as high as $2.50 and $3.00 per lb.

One night Alex and Jack were in charge of the sugar camp, boiling down. Alex had lain down in the bunk of the shack to take a short nap while Jack attended the fires and to the boiling.

Suddenly a snuffling accompanied by a clatter at one end of the camp, where some pots and pails which had been used in the previous day's "sugaring off" had been left standing in a pile. A dark form rose up from amongst them as Jack gave a shout, and a black bear made off rapidly into the woods.

At the noise Alex was awakened and sprang out of the camp. "A bear! A bear!" cried Jack. "He was right there licking those pots!" pointing to where the pile of vessels lay.

Jack grabbed a shot gun which the boys had brought to camp and made off after the bear. But the bear tracks were quickly lost in the gloom of the forest and Jack was compelled to return to camp. " I am going home to get the rifle, Alex !" said Jack, " and then I'm going over to get Dick Everett and his hounds and then we'll get the bear !"

" Oh ! You'll never get him ! Anyway send out Guy to take your place here at the fires while you are away !" replied his brother.

As it was now nearing daylight, Jack quickly made his way home, and securing his rifle and his setter dog Toby, he hastened over to one of the nearby settlers, named Dick Everett, to acquaint Dick of the situation. Dick had but just gotten out of bed on Jack's arrival at his shack and readily agreed to accompany him after bear meat.

Dick was but a comparatively recent arrival as a settler in that part of the township. He had a craving for hunting and had a famous pair of hounds—" Blucher " and " Nero."

Procuring his rifle and calling his dogs to his side, the two men made their way into Beaumont's woods.

" Was he a big fellow, Jack ?" asked Dick.

" I did not see him plainly owing to the darkness, but Alex was closer and he says he was a whale ! Alex says when he rose up from the pots and pans he seemed to be as high as the end of the camp and you know that is over six feet high !" declared Jack.

They quickly reached the sugar camp, where Alex and Guy were now busy with the fires and boiling sap. They scouted around a bit putting the dogs on the bear's trail. The bear tracks were certainly large and indicated a full-grown animal.

The dogs quickly gave tongue and dashed off into the woods, " Blucher " in the lead. Daylight had now come for some time, and objects were plainly seen, and the bear's trail could be easily followed in the snow.

It led at first down into a marshy " swale " filled with clump cedars and catkins. After crossing this it kept along a ridge of land until it entered some thickets.

Here the hounds bayed a good deal and beat about the undergrowth—the bear having evidently lain down here for a time. Shortly the dogs appeared to have picked up the trail and dashed out on the farther side of the thickets and dashed away up a rocky ridge, leading into some hilly and broken country.

Presently the barking of the dogs increased in volume and seemed to come from a fixed point. Dick and Jack dashed up the trail and shortly arrived before a pile of rocks, at the base of a hillside, around which the hounds and Toby were making a great clatter—dashing towards an opening in the rocks, barking and rushing off again.

On making a survey of the place they discovered the bear had made his den in this pile of rocks, an opening between two of the rocks apparently leading to it. The question then was, how to dislodge the bear.

Jack ascended the pile of rocks and with a long pole found he could poke down in the interstices between the rocks upon the bear. The bear now and then emitted a deep growl.

The dogs meanwhile were dashing in and out of the entrance, while Dick was manœuvring out front, endeavouring to get sight of the bear and a shot.

All at once the bear dashed out of his den and in a flash sprang upon Dick. A hasty shot fired by Dick only wounded the animal in the shoulders and served but to infuriate the beast the more. One smash of his powerful paws broke the rifle and Dick's shoulder at the same time, and instantly Dick was down and the bear, grasping him in his fore-paws in a death hug, proceeded to tear him with his teeth and jaws.

Matters now were tremendously serious. Jack dropped his pole and grabbed his rifle and dashed off the rock pile and to one side in an endeavour to get a shot without endangering Dick.

The dogs meanwhile dashed in and out at the bear, nipping him on the flank, and the terrier Toby fastened on to the upper and back part of the bear's thigh—the pain of which caused the animal to leave Dick and turn on the little dog. One swipe of the bear's paw and the whole side of the little dog was ripped open and the faithful animal in a couple of gasps sobbed out his life for his devotion.

This interruption gave Jack his chance, and dropping on one knee, he plumped a rifle ball behind the right fore-leg of the bear, and with a convulsive spring the animal dropped dead.

He was a huge male; close on six feet long and with a thick black hide.

Jack now turned his attention to poor Dick. The latter lay on the ground partly conscious, his right shoulder smashed and with the stock of his rifle broken off from the barrel.

" Are you in much pain, Dick?" anxiously enquired Jack. " Are you suffering?"

Dick opened his eyes, which were almost closed, and muttered—

" Oh! Great pain in my shoulder!" and promptly fainted. Jack grabbed some snow and rubbed Dick's face with it and pressed some between the lips, and presently Dick again opened his eyes.

On examining the shoulder, Jack found the shoulder blade smashed and the arm-bone broken close to the shoulder-joint.

Jack then gathered hemlock brush for Dick to lie upon and support his head, also a pile to shelter him from the wind, and then clearing the ground of snow to the lee of where Dick lay, made a fire of brush and wood to keep the wounded man warm, while he went for help.

"You can't walk home, Dick! I must go to the camp and home for help!" said Jack. Dick who had by now recovered from the first shock, replied—

"Oh! I'm all right! I can walk to the camp!" and endeavoured to sit up but in the act his face became ashen white with the pain on moving the injured shoulder and he sank back on the brush with a groan.

"You can't do it! You see you can't!" cried Jack. "Lie quite still here and be comfortable. I'll hurry home, get the oxen and sled and come here with help for you!" So saying he rapidly made his way back to the sugar camp, relating to his brothers, Guy and Alex, what had occurred. On hearing this Guy ordered Alex to remain at the boiling, while he would go to Dick and remain until Jack had returned with the oxen. Describing to Guy how to find Dick, Jack left on the run for the Beaumont homestead.

There he told his father what had happened and hastily securing oxen and sleigh with bed-clothes for covers, left for the scene of the encounter with the bear.

Here they found Guy and Dick's hounds—who had remained by their master. Tenderly lifting up Dick, they placed him on a bed of hay in the bottom of the sleigh and took him to his home.

After placing him on his bed an examination of his shoulder was made by John Beaumont.

" It's pretty badly smashed and the least move causes grating of the broken bones !" he said, amidst Dick's groans.

" I don't like it !   It's too deep for my ' surgery ' !   I think it best to get a doctor from Durham or Goderich !"

Kubassey.   Niwash.

TWO INDIANS.

A consultation was then held with some of the neighbours who had dropped in.   Jack said Kubassey and Peter Niwash had been camped at the River the day before, that if they could be found they could come up river to Buck's Crossing and then back track to Durham as being the more expeditious method of getting a medical man to see the sufferer, rather than going down stream to the Mouth and then making the long Lake voyage, coasting the east shore of Lake Huron to Goderich.

The former place was resolved upon as best and Jack and Guy left to hunt up the Indians, while John Beaumont made some rough splints of split cedar, and with these as supports bandaged them to the arm and shoulder, but Dick Everett spent a painful night.

The next morning the limb had swollen to a great size. Mr. Beaumont removed the bandages and splints and bathed the parts in cold water. This gave great relief and Dick declared eased the pain considerably. The splints were then re-applied.

In the meantime the Indians—Kubassey and Niwash —had been found up river the evening before. On briefly relating what had occurred and the necessity of seeing a doctor, the Indians promised to set off at once for Durham for the doctor.

With the windings of the river, Durham was all of 50 miles away. Embarking in their birch canoe they proceeded with all speed up the river and paddling the whole night through, reached Buck's Crossing early the next morning.

Here, leaving their canoe in charge of the good-natured settler, Abraham Buck, they set off with the untiring Indian lope for Durham, eleven miles away to the eastwards, through swamps, across streams and over gravelly hills and reached the settlement at midday.

Here the first person they met proved to be George Jackson, the Crown Lands Agent, and on telling him what had occurred and what their errand was he took them to a small log house nearby, where dwelt Dr. Gun, sole medical man of the settlement and of the country between there and Fergus, 50 miles to the south. Dr. Gun at that time was a man of about 40 years, short and stout with dark hair and eyes and a bluff manner.

" Who is the man who is hurt and how?" he inquired. The Indians told him. " Where?" he next asked.

" Down river! Heap bad!" declared Kubassey.

" How am I to get there?"

" Canoe from Buck!" said Peter Niwash, motioning with his hand to the westward.

" Yes, that's right enough, but how am I to get over the 11 miles from here to Buck's Crossing?"

Peter pointed to his feet and said " Very good horse there!"

" I'm not going to tramp to Buck's and back on Shank's mare!" declared the doctor.

" I'll tell you what to do!" spoke up George Jackson, who was ever solicitous for the welfare of the settlers, " I'll go to Jim Hunter and borrow his horse for you! You can leave the animal with Abraham Buck until you return from the river trip to Beaumont's."

It was then so arranged. The horse procured and saddled, the doctor departed accompanied by the two taciturn Indians and they reached Abraham Buck's home by evening. Here, leaving the horse in Buck's charge, the doctor entered on the canoe trip with the Indians and passed swiftly down the river—passing Walker's Settlement at the Clay Banks by ten o'clock that night and reaching Everett's Landing by midnight.

On reaching the latter's house the doctor found a number of the neighbouring settlers gathered there. Making a hasty examination of the injured shoulder, the doctor's verdict was the same as John Beaumont's, that the shoulder blade had been split and the arm-bone broken, and declared that whoever had adjusted the splints and treated the limb had done as good a job as any doctor could do—in short his journey to see the patient was entirely unnecessary, as the proper treatment for the injured limb had been given. This, of course, everyone was glad to hear and many an approving glance was cast in John Beaumont's direction who pshawed! and reddened at the compliment. The doctor assured Everett the limb had had proper attention, that it would be several weeks in healing and that later on easy movement of the joint was essential, that there might be no rigidity, etc., etc.

Getting some supper the doctor asked for a bed and, getting a few hours sleep was ready after an early breakfast at Everett's for the water journey to Buck's with the Indians.

Bidding adieu to the patient and John Beaumont, he entered the canoe—which the Indians held in waiting, and passed rapidly up the river reached Buck's Crossing again by midday. Here securing his horse and bidding adieu to Kubassey and Niwash, he rode off on the trail to Durham while the two Indians turning their canoe headed down stream for their home.

CHAPTER XXIII.

The Race to the Land Office.

Philip Neubecker's Lot adjoined John Beaumont's on the west, but farther down the river. Still farther down Gottlieb Haag had taken up his land and on the same side of the stream. Abutting on Neubecker's Lot, but across the concession line, was a very desirable 100 acres, covered with heavy timber and known as Lot 9, which had not as yet been " squatted " upon or taken up.

Stephen Neubecker had several times urged his father to go to Durham and take up the Lot at the Land Office, of which George Jackson was Crown Lands Agent. This the father had neglected to do.

One evening Steve went over to Beaumonts' for a social call, and while there Guy had told him Jack Haag had been there the evening before, and had stated that on the next day or the day following he intended going to Durham—to the Land Office—to take up Lot 9.

" Now that is very mean business on Haag's part," said Steve. " He knows very well that father intends taking up that Lot for me, as it abuts on our land, while it is some distance from his land. Also, he knows it is a Land Office rule to give the settler first choice of purchasing 100 or 150 acres of land abutting on the first grant. I call that very mean business !" exclaimed Steve.

" Yes, it is, Steve," said Guy, " but I'll tell you what I'd do if I were you. Make an early start for Durham to-morrow morning. You can make the Land Office by night if you hurry, and you may get in ahead of Jack. I saw his father this afternoon, and he told me Jack was going to Durham one of these days."

" I don't know if I could make it in a day," said Steve.

" Sure you could! Kubassey and Pete Niwash have camped down there by the river the past week hunting and trapping. Engage them to take you by canoe to Buck's Crossing. From Buck's Crossing to Durham you can easily make afoot," said Guy. " Don't let Haag beat you, Steve."

" Well, I must see father first," said Steve.

" Well, I wouldn't lose a minute. I'd start off to-night. I tell you what!" said Guy with excitement. " Go and see your father and I'll interview the Indians —they know the river like a book. While the distance from here to Buck's Crossing through the ' Bush ' is about 15 miles, by the river and following its windings it will be all of twice that distance. However, you will be under no exertion, the Indians will do the paddling, so that when you reach the crossing you will be fresh, while Haag, if he starts to morrow morning, will be pretty tired after travelling 15 miles of bush road."

" Get busy and make a start," said Guy. Stephen therefore hurried to his home and acquainted his father with the facts. The old man was very much put out to think a neighbour would endeavour to " steal a march " upon him in the matter of Lot 9, for in the backwoods it was a rule never to infringe the rights— known or implied—of a settler.

" Make a pack of food, Stephen, and take a blanket

and get away to-night. If possible, have the Indians canoe you up river to Buck's. Here is ten pounds, which pay to George Jackson as a first deposit on the land, and have the Registration made out in your name," said old Philip.

Steve accordingly made up a large pack of cold meat, bread, hard-boiled eggs and tea and milk. This he enclosed in a heavy pillow case and again in a double blanket and rolled into a pack, which he slung to his shoulders by a couple of pack straps, and made off for the Indian camp.

On reaching the latter, he found the Indians preparing for the journey and Guy Beaumont still there. A large birch bark canoe was moored to the river bank close to the Indian wigwams. Into this was thrown two pairs of light paddles, some blankets, some jerked venison and their guns, and the party embarked.

" Get him to Buck's as soon as possible, John," said Guy. " I want to see him beat Jack Haag."

" White man at Crossing when sun stand there to-morrow," said Kubassey, pointing with his finger directly overhead.

Good-byes were exchanged and the canoe shoved off. The night was clear with a bright moon riding high in the heavens overhead. The broad river stretched away to the southward, its placid surface gleaming clear in the bright moonlight, while the dark and silent forest clothed either shore. The Indians—one in the bow and the other in the stern of the canoe—plied their paddles incessantly.

The light bark floated on the water like thistle-down, gliding noiselessly forward under the impulse of the paddles.

Now and then from far down the river the distant call

of a loon was heard or the mournful cry of a whippoor-will in the dark forest stretching back from the silent shores.

Midnight came and went as the long reaches of the river were passed over. Just at midnight they passed Jos. Walker's Settlement at the Clay Banks. Passing these banks the river still held to the southwards, but some time after on rounding a bend its direction became north-east. Another hour of paddling found them travelling more to the eastwards.

" Anin endasso—dabaiganeg?" (What time is it?) asked Peter Niwash from the stern of the canoe. Looking up at the stars, Kubassey replied :

" Nio-dabaigen!" (about 4 o'clock). The moon was now hanging low in the western sky, and a slight lighting of the eastern sky indicated daylight was not far distant. There was a chill in the air.

" Isn't it about time we had something to eat, Peter?" said Steve. " I'm hungry. Draw into the bank there and let us eat." The Indian nodded and directed the canoe to the shore, where a landing was made. They jumped ashore, the canoe moored to the bank, and Steve's pack unrolled and the food passed around.

After a hasty repast the canoe was again launched and the journey again resumed. The grey light of early morning was beginning to show in the eastern sky.

Shortly after daybreak they met two canoes coming from the east and loaded with four men in each canoe. The leading canoe had two Indians paddling, one fore and the other aft, and two white men who were land-seekers—Charley Champagne and Michael Laborde, Frenchmen on their way to the western part of the township. The second canoe was also paddled by two Indians and also held two other white men, Larry Duffy, one an old acquaintance from Woolwich, and a Henry Durke from the same township.

" Bon jour! Bon jour, Steve!" cried Champagne, motioning to the Indians to stop paddling. " How far is it to Joe Walker's Settlement?"

" About three hours' run in the canoe, having the current of the river with you," replied Steve.

" You have land?" inquired Champagne.

" Yes, about three hours' run down river from Walker's," replied Steve. " Are you seeking land?"

" Mais oui!" replied the Frenchman. " We go first to Joe Walker; if not suit there, then we go farther down," and with a wave of his hand the canoe passed on.

By noon Steve's canoe made the crossing, and after instructing the Indians to await his return from Durham—probably a few days—landed and struck south to Abraham Buck's log house.

Buck was at home, and remembered Stephen Neubecker from two years before when he had first gone through into the Bush. He inquired as to his father and mother and the Beaumont family, and was greatly pleased to hear they had found good land and were prospering. There was a good trail eastwards from Buck's Crossing to Durham, which lay about 12 miles away.

On inquiring of Buck and giving a minute description of Jack Haag, Abraham Buck declared such a looking man had passed his cabin that morning with a small pack slung on his back and travelling eastwards at a good pace. He estimated the man would then (it was then noon) be about Camp Creek, which lay about 6 miles to the eastward of Buck's house.

This information made Steve very uneasy and he determined to set out at once for Durham, although Buck endeavoured to have him stay for dinner. Therefore, shouldering his pack and thanking Buck for his offered hospitality, Steve set out briskly eastwards.

The trail from Buck's led directly eastward for about a mile over level land, at which point at the angle of an intersecting side road was built a log tavern—Campbell's Corners.

On reaching the Corners, Steve noticed through the open doorway of the log tavern Jack Haag standing before the "bar" with an uplifted glass of whisky in his hand. On hearing Steve's footfalls Haag turned, and seeing Steve, said, "Hello, Neubecker! Come in and have a horn. I suppose you are on the way to the Land Office to get that wood lot, but I'm going to beat you to it!" declared Haag, bringing his fist down upon the "bar" with a bang. It was seen at once that Haag was under the influence of liquor.

Stephen therefore entered the bar-room and, not to seem unsociable, took a small glass of whisky and water, and then "treated" Haag and Campbell, the tavern keeper, in his turn, so that the former could not bring the charge of niggardliness against him.

Haag drank pure whisky—no water for him—and was evidently fast becoming intoxicated, as well as ugly.

"I tell you what, Neubecker! Sit down here and we will play a game of poker for that lot, the winner to take it. Come, now, be a man!" cried Haag.

"No," said Steve. "I must be on my way; besides, I don't know how to play cards."

"Oh, you don't. The innocent fair-haired boy! You're a snivelling, psalm-singing hypocrite, Neubecker! A goody-good boy who will only consort with goody-good girls like Alice Beaumont!"

Neubecker's face went white at this insult.

"Haag, don't say that again, or I'll cram the lie down your throat! Miss Beaumont is a friend of mine, and only a friend, and if you mention her name again in such a connection I'll thrash you soundly. You know I can do it!" and the angry man turned away.

Scarcely had he done so when he heard a shout uttered by the tavern keeper, and turning to see the cause, received a blow on the side of the head which stretched him senseless on the bar-room floor.

On Steve turning away from Haag the latter had seized the heavy brown earthenware pitcher standing on the bar and holding water, and hurled it with all his strength at Neubecker's head.

"You measly hound!" yelled the tavern keeper, Colin Campbell, at Haag, "to strike a man behind his back! Get out of my house, and be thankful I don't kick you out. There's the road. Vamoose!" and he came out from behind the bar and began rolling up his sleeves preparatory to throwing Haag out of the house.

Haag immediately left, staggering off down the road to Camp Creek.

The noise of the affair had in the meantime brought other inmates of the tavern into the room—Jack Campbell, brother of Colin, Tom, Bill and George Baillie, and Bill McMahon.

"Who is this, Colin?" asked Jack Campbell of his brother, and looking at the prostrate form of Stephen.

"I don't know," replied Colin. "That fellow that

knocked him out with the water pitcher called him
Neubecker. I don't know where he is from."

A pail of cold water and a towel were brought, and
Colin Campbell bathed Steve's head and forced some
whisky between the clenched teeth.

Presently Steve came to, sat up, rubbed his sore head
and stared around him, and as recollection came back
to him muttered :—

"This is the second time Jack Haag has tried to
murder me."

"Was that his name?" asked Campbell. "He's a
dirty dog, whoever he is!"

Stephen then asked what had become of Haag. "I
ordered him out of the house," said Campbell. "He
took the road to Durham after knocking you out."

Stephen then recounted what had happened at the
Raising the previous year, also his errand to Durham,
and remarked in a down-hearted manner, "Then Haag
has won the bush lot and my father will be greatly disappointed, as he intended the lot for my farm. I can't
hope to overtake Haag now before he reaches Durham
and the Land Office."

"You never can tell, my boy!" said Colin Campbell.
"There's many a slip betwixt the cup and the lip.
Cheer up! Drink a bowl of hot soup and get on your
way to the Land Office."

The soup was quickly brought and drunk, and finding his strength restored, Steve was uneasy to be on
his way. Finally thanking the kind Campbell brothers
he again took the trail eastwards.

The Western sun was casting long shadows to the
east as he entered the hilly country to the east of
Campbell's Corners on his way to Durham. His head
ached, and at times he had dizzy spells come on him,

so that for the first couple of miles he had frequently
to sit down and rest. These spells, however, became
fewer as he went on, so that by nightfall, when he
reached Devine's Tavern at Camp Creek, they had left
him.

Devine's Tavern was a log structure situated in the
hollow close to Camp Creek and on its eastern side.
Lights now poured from its windows and open door,
and a group of men were gathered about the latter.

Steve made his way through the crowd and entered
the bar-room, which was full of men. Standing at the
bar and with his coat off, a glassful of whisky in his
hand and boasting of his prowess as a ñghter, stood
Jack Haag.

At sight of him Steve's gorge arose. Resentment at
all the injuries and insults he had suffered at the hands
of this man rose up in him; a compelling anger took
possession of him, and he cried out :—

"You are a coward and a liar, Haag! You tried to
murder me twice by foul means! Come outside, and
I will show these people the kind of a fighter you are!"

Turning to the crowded bar-room, Steve said :

"Men, my name is Stephen Neubecker; that man
is Jack Haag. We are both from the western part of
Brant Township. To-day at noon Haag tried by a
foul blow to kill me at Campbell's Corners. He is also
endeavouring to steal away my farm from me. We can
now settle the matter here. Come outside, Haag."

The onlookers, rough men of the woods, were keen
to see a fight. "Come out and fight, Haag!" was the
general cry.

Haag, although evidently in liquor, still was sober
enough to know that he was no match for Stephen
Neubecker, his superior in weight and reach. But he

was forced out by the crowd and began stripping for the fight, surrounded by a few men who were anxious to see the contest.

Haag carefully placed his coat and vest at one end of the tavern building, and in doing so picked up a round stone about the size of a goose egg, which he kept concealed in his right hand.

A ring was formed by the onlookers, with Neubecker on one side and Haag on the other.

" Now, Haag, come on !" yelled Steve and rushed at Haag. The latter took a step forward, whirled his right hand over his head, and hurled the stone with all his force at Neubecker's head. By a miracle it missed Steve, but struck a settler on the other side of the ring of onlookers named Syd Willis in the stomach knocking him down instantly. Pandemonium at once broke loose. " The d-----n hound !" " The treacherous b----r ; kill him, Neubecker !" were the exclamations hurled at Haag. In the meantime the fighters had come together. Steve struck Haag a blow on the side of the head, and then grasped him about the waist and endeavoured to throw him, but Haag squirmed up Steve's body and threw his arms around his neck and began endeavouring to gouge out one of his eyes, at the same time bringing his mouth against Steve's face and endeavouring to bite his nose.

Not succeeding in this he turned his attention to an ear and succeeded in getting a portion of Steve's left ear in his mouth, which he bit off. When Steve by a mighty effort flung Haag from him he struck the ground and lay half-stunned. Recovering, he jumped to his feet and again rushed at Steve. The latter " ducked " low as Haag rushed, and ramming his head between Haag's legs and seizing the latter hurled him over his head backwards, where he struck the ground with his head and remained insensible.

A bucket of water was brought by one of the on-lookers and doused over Haag, who was some time in coming to, the shock had been so great.

On endeavouring to sit up, Haag found the pain in his neck so great he was unable to do so, and fell back on the ground with a groan. " Get up, you b ---- r !" yelled an onlooker. " What you lying there for ?" Haag whined " I can't, I think my neck is broken !" feeling the lower part of his neck, where on the right side a large swelling was already rising.

" D ---- n good job if your neck is broken !" said another settler. " Fellers like you shouldn't be allowed to live ! You damn near killed Syd Willis with that stone you threw !"

Poor Syd was sitting in a chair in the bar-room to which he had been carried, doubled up with pain. Devine, the tavern keeper, was plying him with hot whisky, his one and only cure for all the ailments of the human race.

Steve meantime was bathing his torn ear, the upper half of which was gone. " I suppose the b ---- r ate it !" cried another settler. " The d ---- n brute looks as if he could live on human flesh !"

Matt Devine now went over to Haag and examined his neck and found he had broken his right collar-bone, no doubt due to the fall.

" Your collar-bone is busted !" said Devine. " Sit up, and I will tie up your arm in a sling."

With many groans Haag was gotten to a sitting position; a sheet from the tavern was torn to make a sling, and Haag was supported into the bar-room, where he asked for a bedroom to lie down in. This was given him.

During this time Steve had succeeded in stopping the bleeding from the ear, and, after some supper at the tavern, decided to push on for Durham that night.

Matt Devine endeavoured to persuade him to remain overnight at the tavern, saying there was no occasion now for hurry, as Haag couldn't walk far with his busted shoulder. However, Steve decided to go, and after taking a hearty handshake from the kindly Boniface, bade him farewell and took the trail again eastwards. But the effects of the blow on the head at Campbell's Tavern, together with the loss of blood from the torn ear, had made him weaker than he had estimated, so that on reaching Livingstone's Tavern, $2\frac{1}{2}$ miles from Durham, at about 10 o'clock, he was glad to take bed and shelter there for the night.

Next morning, being haunted with the thought Haag might be before him at the Land Office, he arose early and again took to the road, and reached Durham and was at George Jackson's office before 7 o'clock.

On the latter coming down and opening the door, Steve told him his errand and was at once admitted; the particulars of the Lot and Concession entered; his name put down on the Registration; the money paid over and he was given his Registration receipt, and shaking Mr. Jackson's hand and thanking him, departed for Hunter's Hotel for needed rest and refreshment.

CHAPTER XXIV.

The Fight at Campbell's Corners.

After spending a couple of days in Durham at Hunter's Tavern Steve decided to return home. After an early breakfast at the backwoods hostelry he started for Camp Creek on the morning of the third day, and reached Devine's Tavern along towards noon.

Here he learned from Devine that Haag had taken the back track for Brant on the day following his fight with Steve. Devine said Haag was morose and moody on the morning following the fight, and had said he had spent a sleepless night because of the pain of his broken collar-bone, and that he was returning home, and after paying his bill had left.

Bidding Devine good-bye, Steve then pushed on for the crossing, and at about 3 o'clock arrived at Campbell's Tavern at the Corners. Here before the log tavern a number of men were gathered—Colin Campbell; his brother, John Campbell; Tom, Bill and George Baillie; Andy McFarlane and Bill McMahon. "Oh, here's the boy from Brant!" cried Bill Baillie, addressing Steve. "How did you make out in Durham? Did you get your wood Lot?"

"Yes, I'm registered for the Lot," replied Steve.

"And what became of that fellow Haag?" inquired John Campbell.

Steve then recounted to the men the incidents which had occurred at Devine's Tavern at Camp Creek on his way to Durham, and how Haag had received a broken collar-bone, and three days before had returned to Brant.

"I didn't see him pass here. He must have gone through in the night," said Colin Campbell.

"Good job, too!" said John Campbell. "We don't want any man here who would strike another behind his back."

"There are some men, though, over at Joe Walker's Settlement in Brant who would strike you in the back!" declared Colin Campbell, hotly.

"Yes. They are trying to strike us in the back now, but they won't succeed!" said Andy McFarlane, with some heat.

"How is that?" asked Steve.

"A skunk named Benson, and calling himself a bailiff, stole my span of horses in the northern part of Brant Township, and spirited them away to Walker's Settlement at the Clay Banks, where a couple of us went and retrieved them. And now we hear a couple of constables are on their way here to arrest us for it. Arrest us for taking possession of our own property!" said Andy McFarlane. "We are just setting out to meet the constables and give them a proper welcome, so we will bear you company, Neubecker, as far as the river!" cried Bill McMahon.

The company, consisting of seven men, then set out westwards for the crossing, about a mile away. Reaching the crossing nothing was seen on the farther side of the river. Secreting themselves in bushes by the roadside, the seven met sat down to await the coming of the minions of the law.

Steve decided it would be the part of wisdom to wait also, as he did not believe the gang would allow him to continue his journey westwards and perhaps warn the constables of what awaited them.

A half-hour had scarcely passed when two men were observed coming along the roadway from the west towards the crossing. This they passed over, but had scarcely done so when they were surrounded by the gang—each man armed with a gun.

Colin Campbell in a loud voice demanded their names and business.

" My name is Caleb Huyck," said one of the men, " and this man is George Simpson.   We are Special Constables bearing a warrant signed by Judge Cooper to arrest the Campbell brothers, Colin and John and Andy McFarlane, for breaking into the tavern stables at Walker's Settlement and removing therefrom a span of horses held by due process of law," declared Huyck.

" The h - - - l you say !" shouted Andy McFarlane. " Produce your warrant."

Huyck produced his warrant and, unfolding it, showed it to them.

" Now tear it up !" said Andy McFarlane, pointing his gun at the constable.

Huyck protested. " You are opposing the law. That is a penitentiary offence. Have a care what you do !"

" And I tell you," said McFarlane, " have a care what you do !   If you do not tear up that warrant before I count five I will fire a charge of buckshot into your body !" and he brought his gun to bear on the constable a few feet away, and began counting in a loud voice. Huyck therefore reluctantly tore up the warrant.

" Now I'll take a hand, Huyck," said Colin Campbell. " You eat up every one of those pieces of the warrant, or I'll fill you full of lead !" and Campbell pointed his double-barrel shot-gun at the constable's legs and drew back the hammer. Huyck, of course, demurred, thereupon Campbell fired one of the barrels of his gun into the roadway, beside Huyck's feet, scattering some gravel over him in doing so.

CONSTABLE EATING WARRANT.

"Now get busy, or I'll give you the other barrel into your legs, my buck! Eat!" cried Campbell. Huyck hastily grabbed at the torn pieces of the warrant, and cramming them into his mouth began swallowing them. "Ho! ho! See the b----r swallow! What a different meal from the last one you had, Huyck! Does it taste good? Like some pepper and salt with it?" and Bill McMahon went off into roars of laughter at the sight of the discomfited constable swallowing his warrant.

This put the rest of the gang in good humour, and Colin Campbell, turning to the constables, said :

" Now you men better return to whence you came, and be thankful you have gotten off with whole skins. Many another in our place would have filled you full of lead. We are the law here. Never again interfere in the affairs of honest men. There's the road—go !" and he pointed across the river.

Needless to say, Huyck and Simpson quickly retreated across the Saugeen and then took the road westwards.

Gazing after the retreating figures of the constables for a time, Colin Campbell remarked, " It's pretty certain these men will return to Walker's and secure reinforcements and that we will be attacked in force to-morrow."

" Let us get back to the tavern and prepare for it. As for you, Neubecker, if you return by Walker's Settlement—there is no other way to your home—you are sure to be impressed and sworn in to act as a Special Constable and come against us, when you will be shot," said Colin. " Better come along and throw in your lot with us."

" No," said Steve. " I've no quarrel with the law and do not wish to be a party to one, but as I can't get by Walker's without being impressed, I will remain over here for a day, but not take any part in any fight."

The party then returned to Campbell's Tavern, where the evening was spent in jollity, card playing and drinking, with fiddle playing and step dancing being the chief amusements, and kept up until a late hour in the night.

Next morning Steve arose early and took a stroll around. It was a beautiful morning in June, and as the sun arose in the east it threw a bright sheen upon the miles and miles of green foliage extending off in the forest to the east and south. Here and there a smoke arose from a few spots in the green foliage, indicating where some settler was beginning his daily toil at clearing the forest.

The Durham road extended away eastward in a narrow winding lane between two banks of forest green.

Returning to the log tavern, breakfast was had and then Colin Campbell said, " Now, men, we are due for a lively time to-day and must prepare for it. I judge that crowd from Walker's will be along here about midday, and I propose to give them a lively reception. They propose to take me and my brother John prisoners, but I propose they won't. Now what will you men do? Will you back me up in it?" and he looked keenly at the faces around him.

" Fight them !" declared Andy McFarlane and Bill McMahon with one voice. " Fight them to the last drop. The horses they claim are mine. They have no authority here. We are in Grey County and they are in Bruce. County officials and their warrant is only legal in Bruce and not here."

" Yes, they are bulldozers and full of conceit," said John Campbell, " but we will take the conceit out of them."

Preparations then began to receive the posse of constables. Doors were barricaded by means of heavy articles of furniture placed against them and windows were partially boarded up, leaving enough space in the latter to shove a gun through. Buckets of water were

then brought into the tavern so as to be on hand in case
of fire.

" The only danger is in the lean-to at the back of the
tavern," declared Colin Campbell. " They may reach
that from the woods, which runs close to the building,
and succeed in entering or setting fire to the buildings."

To prevent this two men, John Campbell and Tom
Baillie, were sent to the attic, where through a small

FIGHT AT CAMPBELL'S CORNERS.

window they could watch for any assault upon the
lean-to attached to the back of the building. Downstairs two men were placed with guns near the doors
at the front and back, while another man was deputed
to load the guns lying upon a large table in the centre
of the room.

These preparations took up most of the forenoon and
still no enemy appeared in the offing. A hasty meal
was cooked and partaken of, and the inmates of the

tavern fortress awaited the advent and onslaught of the minions of the law. During these preparations Steve began to think seriously of his own position.

He was determined to do no act that would oppose the law and to take no part in the forthcoming fight. Therefore, seeking out a corner of the lower room farthest from the front door and out of what would probably be the direct line of fire in case of shooting, he ensconced himself therein, a neutral spectator of the struggle.

About noon a large party of men were seen, armed with guns and rifles, advancing from the west. These presently drew up in front of the tavern, and a Magistrate a Mr. Jamieson from Walker's Settlement— drew out a warrant and hailed the building.

" Colin and John Campbell and Andrew McFarlane, I hold in my hand a warrant properly executed by constituted authority for your arrest. Come out and surrender !" cried the Magistrate.

Colin Campbell replied, " We are honest men and you shall not arrest us. Your warrant has no force in this County. Get away from my property or suffer the consequences !" and he shoved a gun out of a window.

The Magistrate continued, " Now, Campbell, you are opposing the law which we must all obey. It is the duty of every good citizen to obey the law. This is a free country, and a man has a perfect right to express an opinion, but there is a limit beyond which no man can go. He must not follow up that opinion by armed resistance to constituted authority. Surrender and save yourselves from worse !" cried the Magistrate.

" We will not surrender, and if you attack us you must take the consequences !" declared Campbell.

While this harangue was in progress some of the

13

posse had surrounded the house, and some of them, taking cover in the surrounding forest, advanced at the back to the lean-to and set fire to some dry brush, which they threw against the building. This quickly took fire and spread upwards to the roof, which began crackling, and dense volumes of smoke rolled up. This drew the attention of the men in the attic—John Campbell and Tom Baillie—who, opening the small window overlooking the lean-to, discharged several shots into the bush behind the tavern. This was the signal for a general fusillade from both the attackers and the attacked.

"Bring up water—the lean-to is on fire!" cried John Campbell, going to the stairway and shouting down to his comrades below.

This was quickly done, and pail after pail of water was hastily thrown through the small window upon the burning roof below.

Presently the flames ceased, but volumes of dense smoke enveloped the tavern, lit up by the occasional flashes of the guns of the besieged as they continued firing from the beleaguered fortress below.

As the smoke cleared away the firing ceased, and again the Magistrate—standing behind a tree—shouted to the Campbells to surrender or they would burn the building over their heads. The only reply to this from the Campbells was a volley from the guns facing the front, which caused chips of bark to fly from the tree behind which His Honour was taking refuge. Desultory firing kept up for a time and finally died away. The attackers then retreated from around the building and held a council of war.

"The devils are concocting some new scheme to burn us out!" said Colin Campbell. "I'm sorry I didn't get in a greater supply of water. All the pails are empty, and the full barrel of water we had there has not more than half a dozen pails left.''

"We will have to watch the lean-to with more care and shoot down any man who approaches it. That's the only place where they can attack us with fire,'' said George Baillie.

Three men were then sent into the attic with all the water that could be gotten, while the men below awaited a renewal of the attack. This was some time in coming, and presently the sound of axes and hammering was heard.

"What deviltry are they up to now?'' said John Campbell.

"Building their own coffins probably!'' said Bill McMahon. "They will sure need them if I get a bead on any of them, for I'm going to shoot to kill.''

The attacking force now spread around the tavern again, keeping as much as possible behind the cover of trees, and began a tremendous firing at the windows and doors of the main building. To this the besieged made a vigorous reply. When the fusillade was at its highest pitch, George Baillie, on looking out of the attic window, exclaimed : "What devil's work are they up to now? There's a side of a barn approaching the lean-to!'' and he pointed downwards through the window.

The remark was not literally true, but on first sight appeared so. The besiegers in their council of war had seen that the lean-to was the only vulnerable point of attack in the log tavern. To tear off the large door of the log stable hard by the tavern was the work of a few moments; to attach cross-pieces to its back capable of allowing four men to carry it forwards as a shield against the shots of the besieged and cast fire against the out-building from its shelter was quickly decided upon as the surest means of ousting the defiers of the law from their nest. This was now done.

Shot after shot was poured into the advancing door by the tavern inmates, but without avail. It slowly advanced against the lean-to, which it struck and rested, when from behind its shelter blazing brush and faggots were cast against the dry side-wall boards of the lean-to. This quickly blazed up, while some men with guns belonging to the constable's posse took up a position in the woods to the back of the tavern and poured shot after shot into the attic window overlooking the lean-to. Though pail after pail of water was thrown out of the windows, because of the shots these could not be accurately aimed at the flames, and finally, as the supply of water ran out, the flames secured a firm hold upon the shed, and rapidly mounting attacked the roof of the main building, which was presently a mass of flames.

The men in the attic now retreated to the main floor below and reported the roof to be on fire, and that the building would have to be abandoned.

"Well, boys," said Colin Campbell, "we must make a dash for it to the woods. The wind is from the South. Let us wait until the smoke becomes thick and blowing more to the north, which will practically conceal us, when I will open the door and make a rush down the side road and into the bush. Follow me when I rush, and shoot down any man who attempts to stop you!"

The heavy cupboard was now removed from the door and the party waited until the smoke grew denser. The crackling of the burning roof overhead now gave place to a deep roar as the whole roof became embraced by the flames, and the brown smoke rolled in dense masses down the roadway.

" Now !" cried Colin Campbell, as, throwing open the door, he dashed out and into the smoke and down the roadway to the north at top speed, and followed by the Baillies—Tom, George and Bill—John Campbell, Andy McFarlane, and Bill McMahon last.

A fusillade of shots was poured out by the besiegers as the figures vanished in the smoke, and Bill McMahon gave a yell and clapped his hand to his leg but kept running, and escaped into the surrounding bush. When the gang had retreated sufficiently far to be out of gun-shot, it was found Bill McMahon had received a buckshot in the fleshy part of the right thigh and Colin Campbell several buckshot in the back.

" We must work back more into the woods," said Colin Campbell, unmindful of his wounds, " and fight them off if they attack us. Get behind trees if they come to us and give it to them ! Don't wound, but shoot to kill. We will retreat northwards and secure help and shelter at some of the settlers' shanties."

In the meantime the upper part of the log tavern was now a roaring furnace, and the constables' posse were standing in the roadway gazing on the burning building and speculating as to whether any of the gang had been killed or wounded in the scrimmage. Suddenly the figure of Steve Neubecker appeared in the doorway of the burning building with his arms elevated and crying, " I surrender !" The guns which had been instantly thrown up and aimed at him on his first cry were now lowered.

" Come out here and give an account of yourself, young man !" cried Magistrate Jamieson. Steve, therefore, told his tale—that he was an unwilling inmate of the tavern and had taken no part in the fighting, and was only pursuing his way to his home in Brant Township when he fell in with the gang.

CHAPTER XXV.

PENETANGORE.

As time went on settlement increased. Timber "slashes" gave place to cultivated fields, dotted with stumps. Roadways were chopped out and made passable for wheeled vehicles. A few scattered settlements sprang up. Of these Walker's Settlement at the Clay Banks; Simon Orchard's at the junction of the Yokissippi and Saugeen River, and Penetangore at the mouth of the Penetangore River on Lake Huron, were the chief.

Penetangore, being on the Lake and nearest navigation, its people conceived the idea of building a harbour there, so that vessels could load and unload in safety; and believing it to be in the interest of the whole County the Township Council of that municipality passed a by-law calling for a vote of the ratepayers in the surrounding townships against the cost of building a harbour. This did not at all meet the view of the settlers in the back townships, and they were not backward in making their sentiments known. They believed the harbour to be for the sole benefit of the villagers of Penetangore. Protests were made and a campaign initiated to prevent that village saddling the costs of their undertaking upon the rest of the county. Feeling ran high and indignation was extreme.

The voting upon this project was to take place at Penetangore village on May 28, 1853. An organization of the Townships to the north and east was undertaken to vote the project down. The freeholders from the North—Bruce and Saugeen Townships and the Mouth, came down to Penetangore for the voting mostly by water, in sailing vessels—" The Emily " and the schooner " Sea Gull "; while those from the East—Kinloss, Greenock and Brant Townships—came on foot, in a procession.

This procession started out from Walker's Settlement with Jos. Walker—the founder of the settlement—at its head and riding the solitary horse of the settlement. At Johnston's Corner, 3 miles west of Walker's, a contingent of Western Brant settlers joined the procession —Eckfords, Neelys, Johnstons, Adairs, Everetts, Stewarts, Lamonts and Browns. Here a council of war was held and it was decided that during their visit to the Lake village the settlers would boycott Penetangore as well as vote down its By-law. For this purpose the gathering agreed not to spend a copper in that village during their stay there and to take along their own supplies of food and drink (whisky was an ordinary beverage in those days).

At the halt made at Johnston's Corners several settlers addressed the crowd.

Mounting a stump John Eckford held up his hand.

" Men of Brant, we are joined together to put down selfishness and greed. The Penetangore people wish to tax you for an improvement to their town that will add to their own business and at your expense! Is that fair play? Will you sanction that?" and he smashed his right fist into his left palm.

Shouts of " No!" echoed through the crowd. " King " Johnston sprang on to another stump. " Men!" he shouted " these people at the Lake are hogs! We should not spend a copper amongst them!

Let us agree to take along our own food and drink and not patronize any building or person in Penetangore while we are there. We can secure supplies at Black Horse and be independent of the Penetangore people.''

This was agreed to and the procession re-formed and slowly wound its way westward towards Lake Huron, bearing a banner at its forefront with the motto "Brant! No taxation! No surrender!" By noon it had passed the town of Greenock, its numbers constantly increasing. By 2 p.m. its head had reached what is now Riversdale, where it crossed the Yokissippi River, and by the time it had reached Black Horse, about 4 p.m., it numbered upwards of 400 people.

Our old friends, the Gordons, Neubeckers, Beaumonts and Andy Duffy were there. Charley Champagne and Michael Laborde and all the other free-holders in the western part of Brant were amongst the throng.

At Black Horse, supplies of provisions and liquors were gotten, and these Bruce freemen kept moving steadily westward. There were still 12 miles to go to reach the Lake, but they trudged steadily onwards. An hour later they reached what is now Bervie, and many stopped to refresh themselves at John McKinney's tavern. There were still 7 miles to go and the Crusaders tramped bravely onwards.

By 7 p.m. they had reached Penetangore and the lake and numbers tramped about surveying the town and partaking of their own liquid refreshments. To aggravate the Penetangore Bonifaces, numbers gathered before the log taverns of Paddy Walker and Pat Downie, on the flat near the mouth of the river, where flasks were produced and their contents freely imbibed.

" We carry our own bar room wid us, me buckee!"

shouted Larry Duffy, through the open doorway of Paddy Walker's tavern, to its proprietor, who was standing behind the bar. "How do you like that you Penetangore hogs?"

"Go and wash your mouth, you Irish pig!" said Walker.

"Wash me face is it? Better wash yer own heart, you Scotch gomeril, 'tis black enough wanting other people to pay your debts. Devil a sup or bite will any of us take from ye while we are here, and to-morrow we'll knock your by-law sky high with our vote!" declared Larry.

"By gar! Dat was right Andy!" declared Jos. Chartrand, "dese fellers dey pretty near put hand in your pocket and steal de money!"

"Wait until to-morrow!" said Andy, and turned away.

While this altercation was going on, another large crowd had gathered before Pat Downie's tavern—where the proprietor along with some of the villagers—Allan Cameron, Chris Barker, Alex McKay and George McLeod, were standing.

"You men have a lot of gall to ask us to pay for your harbour!" said John Eckford, addressing the company. "You'll want us to pay for your houses and lots next!"

"It is for your benefit, as well as ours!" hotly replied Allan Cameron. "If we secure a harbour it will prove an easy outlet for your grain, which hitherto you have had to team all the way to Goderich! Have some sense!"

"It will be of very little benefit to us!" angrily retorted King Johnston, "while seven-eighths of the cost will be saddled on to our shoulders! For colossal gall and cheek you Penetangore people take the cake!

Pay for your own improvements, you schemers!" and with a curse he turned away.

In such disputes the time passed. Night drawing on many sought the Lake shore and sought shelter under the cedars and juniper bushes which lined the beach, true to their agreement not to patronize anyone or anything in Penetangore.

That same night a number of Penetangore people gathered at Pat Downie's tavern. "I tell you what it is, boys," declared Bill Rastall, "these fellows from Brant are out for blood! If we don't outwit them they will defeat our by-law!"

"Oh! I don't know!" said Allan Cameron. "The men from Huron Township and the south are all for us, while many freeholders from Bruce Township in the north will vote for us. These with our own votes should give us the majority!" "Don't you believe it!" said Rastall. "Greenock and Brant and Kinloss and the Saugeen Country are all against us and the whole northern end of Bruce Township will vote against us!"

"See here, boys!" continued Rastall, "I'll tell you what to do! Get hold of the Brant Roll and hide it, and without Brant the opposition to the by-law can't win!"

"That wouldn't be a bad idea!" said Chris Barker, but the question is how are we going to get it?"

"I'll tell you!" said Bill Withers, "Rod McDonald is a great chum of 'King' Johnston, and 'King' Johnston has the Roll of Brant. Fill him up with whisky and Rod can 'swipe' the Roll! Then we have them!"

After some further discussion this was agreed to, as it was felt by nearly all that unless Brant Township was eliminated from the contest, their by-law hadn't a ghost of a show of carrying.

Rod McDonald was hunted up and was found in the company of ' King ' Johnston, Joe Walker, George Weir and Alex Stewart in John Keyworth's store where a number of other Penetangorese had gathered, all loudly discussing the coming vote. Rod was taken aside and informed of what was expected of him.

" I don't know if I can do it !" he said. " ' King ' is an old bird and not easy to fool. He has the roll wrapped in brown paper in an inside pocket of his coat ; besides it will take a power of whisky to knock him out ! And how about myself ? I have to set the pace in the drinking and the chances are that I will be down and out before he will ! What will happen then ?" " Don't you worry !" said Bill Rastall, " you get him drunk and there will be someone there to get the Roll !" and with that he turned away.

After a few more arguments—pro and con—had been thrashed out, the Brant people began setting out for the Shore to their night camp, refusing the entreaties of Keyworth, Withers and some others to " put up " with them for the night.

Rod McDonald plucked " King " Johnston by the sleeve and took him outside.

" Now ' King,' you come with me for the night. We are old chums, you know I don't live in Penetangore but in Huron Township. I am only here for the voting but I'm putting in the night at my cousin's, George McLeod's. Come along and sleep with me in a civilized bed and not out there on the cold gravel of the beach ! Besides I have a bottle of French Cognac brandy, brought up from Goderich last week ! You will be my guest and not that of any villager !" said Rod.

" All right !" said King. " I'll go with you ! but I

wouldn't go with anyone else but you, Rod!" They struck down to the south end of the village and entered George McLeod's log house. Mrs. McLeod and a couple of children were the only inmates.

"George not in yet, Mary?" asked Rod. "No!" replied Mrs. McLeod, "he is very late! He is usually home before this hour at nights. But he can't be very long. Sit down and make yourselves at home!" and shaking hands with Mr. Johnston, whom Rod introduced, she placed chairs for them. After a few commonplace remarks, a noise was heard without and George McLeod accompanied by Bill Rastall entered. Conversation now became general and the whisky bottle passed freely around, and soon the party grew hilarious. A game at cards was proposed and the party sat down to a four-handed game of euchre—Rod and King being partners, against Rastall and George McLeod.

As each game was played the bottle circulated around the table, but Bill Rastall indulged very sparingly. The effect of the frequent potations was soon noticeable on King Johnston. He grew more excited and his talk grew louder and he plumped the table with a bang as he played his cards. Finally the game stood 2 and 2 for each side when Rod arose remarking "Oh! I'd nearly forgotten my French Cognac! I'll get it!" and getting up from the table, he went into an adjoining room, from which he presently emerged carrying a bottle of French brandy.

"This will put some life into your playing, boys! Try her!" and he planked the bottle upon the table. The cork was quickly drawn and the liquor served. "King" being the guest was served first with a generous measure. The bottle and glass were then passed around, and each man helped himself. It was noticed that Rastall took very sparingly of the fiery liquor. The cards were then resumed and play went on. As each game was ended the bottle again circulated. The effect of the whisky on Johnston had been to make him extremely excitable but after a couple of rounds of the Cognac he became somniferous, muttering to himself and presently fell forwards with his head upon the table.

The conspirators exchanged significant glances, but the fact of the matter was they were all deeply under the effects of the powerful liquor and not in much better case than Johnston. Rastall alone possessed his senses, due to his moderate potations, and now rising and going around the table he slipped his hand inside Johnston's coat and drew out the precious voters' Roll.

"Now carry him off into a bed and let him sleep it off and you stay with him, Rod. I'm off to John Keyworth's!"

Reaching Keyworth's store Rastall saw a light inside and the proprietor with Alex McKay, Bill Withers and Allan Cameron inside.

"There you are, boys! What do you think of that?" exclaimed Rastall as he slapped the brown packet containing the Brant Voter's Roll upon a counter!

"What is it?" asked Withers. "Why it's the Brant Roll!" said Rastall, "and without it the Brant people can't vote to-morrow!"

"How did you get it?" asked Cameron.

"I got it from Johnston, where he's lying drunk in McLeod's house!" and he laughed a loud guffaw.

"Hurrah!" said Cameron. "That's fine! Now we've got them!"

A consultation was then held and Cameron and Rastall were deputed to bury the Roll in the huge sand dune which at that date separated the Penetangore

River from Lake Huron. This they did and on returning to Keyworth's store, all parties separated for the night, as it was then a late hour and the next day was likely to be a strenuous one.

The voting was to take place in Paddy Walker's Tavern, on the Lake Shore, from the hour of 9 a.m. until 5 p.m. The little village presented a busy sight on that May day in 1853. The "Sea Gull" and the "Emily" had been anchored off the shore during the night and many of the contingent brought down by these vessels from the north had slept on board. These now put off for the shore and the voting in small boats.

The men from the east roused up from their hard couches under the bushes of the Lake shore, shook themselves, took a dram and a snack from the supplies each man carried, and then revived and with freshened energies prepared to "knock-out" the Penetangore Harbour by-law.

Crowds began wending their way to Walker's tavern. There a novel throng had assembled. The long hair, the heavy beards, the gnarled hands, the heavy cowhide boots extending to the knee, inside which the homespun trousers were tucked, whilst the mud-covered boots due to their long trip from Walker's settlement to the Lake, and the rough garb of these backwoodsmen of Bruce, contrasted strongly with the neater garb and shoes of the village-dwellers.

Whisky circulated freely and shortly voices were raised in argument and the crowd fell into groups.

The poll was opened at Paddy Walker's tavern at 9 o'clock, and, taking the Townships alphabetically, the Returning Officer called for the Brant Roll first. This was not forthcoming, and cries for "King" Johnston were passed through the crowd. No Johnston appearing, some men set out to scour the village for him.

Presently he was seen running bare-headed towards Walker's and the polling place. As he joined the throng before the tavern, he shouted " Men, I've been drugged and robbed of the Roll last night ! I had the Roll last night at George McLeod's and this morning it's gone. There's been treachery and foul play here and I think I know who did it. Rastall's the man !"

" You're a 1 - - r !" shouted Alex Munro. " You probably lost it yourself in a drunken fit and now you blame it on one of our villagers !"

This statement led to an altercation between Johnston and Munro, the upshot of which was that the two men rushed at each other and clinched. The uproar now became general. From argument the discussion passed to blows, and many groups in front of the polling place were in a struggling mass.

" This will never do !" said Reeve Fraser of the Penetangore municipality, and quickly picking out 22 men he speedily swore them in as Special Constables, enjoined to keep the peace in the name of the Queen, and to disperse the men to their homes in the different townships.

In the meantime William Gunn and John Valentine, of Walker's Settlement, James Bruson of Brant, Henry Hilker and James Conaway of Southampton and Saugeen, entered a written protest against further proceedings by the Returning Officer, and this stopped further action on the vote.

The crowds gradually scattered. The " Sea Gull " and the " Emily " received their contingents and spread their sails for the north. The men from Greenock and Brant straggled slowly eastwards, taking the Durham Road homewards, and to speak with indignation, for long afterwards, of the action of the Penetangorese—a feeling which it took years to allay.

Two weeks after the above events, Cowan Keyes, the mail carrier between Penetangore and Durham, delivered a brown paper parcel at Walker's Post Office, which he had received at Penetangore. It was directed to Jos. Walker and was the Brant Roll, unearthed from the sand dune.

CHAPTER XXVI.

MER DOUCE (MARE DUCE).

SAMUEL DE CHAMPLAIN, the founder of Quebec, was the discoverer of Upper Canada. Travelling up the Ottawa River from Montreal, with his Huron allies, he reached the Mattewan River, a tributary of the Ottawa. Following this river up to its head waters, he portaged across to Lake Nippissing, and coasted along the Southern shore in bark canoes to the opening of the French river, down which he paddled to its mouth on the Georgian Bay, whose eastern shores he followed southwards to the present Matchedash Bay.

On that July day in the year 1615, when he first landed from his Indian canoe upon the shores of Matchedash Bay, near the present Penetanguishene, he, together with his Indian interpreter, Etienne Brule and Le Caron, the Recollect priest, were the first white men to cast their eyes upon the waters of the Great Lakes.

Gazing out upon the vast expanse of water, which looked like the ocean and which they at first thought might be the sea which led to China, Champlain was filled with wonder and amazement. On tasting the water he found it not salt but fresh—hence he named it Mer Douce, the Sweet Water Sea. Sweet were its waters and sweet were the waters of its sister lakes—a quintette whose like is nowhere else seen in the world.

Its great extent from the far north, where the St. Mary empties the waters of Superior into its bosom, to the far south where St. Ciair pours the flowing tide, onwards to Eerie. From the sandy shores of Michigan on the

14

west to the sounding shores of Huron, Bruce and Manitoulin on the east and with two immense arms—Saginaw
Bay on the west and Georgian Bay on the east, it forms
a sheet of water whose like is not found in older lands.
Hundreds of islands are scattered upon its surface or
dotted along its shores. With its sister bodies of waters
it forms the Great Lakes of North America, one of the
great natural wonders of the world.

The Great Lakes of the North American continent
form the greatest system of fresh-water seas known to the
universe. By their outlet on the east they give access
to the Atlantic and thus form a waterway to the heart of
the North American Continent. To the north, by por-
tages, they give access to the Arctic, and also by por-
tages to Tropic seas in the sunny south; and westwards
by the mighty Saskatchewan to that back-bone of the
Continent—the Rockies, whence streams pour westwards
to Balboa's silent sea—the Pacific. No wonder that
Champlain standing on the shores of blue Mer Douce,
on that July day in 1615, dream't its western shores
might lead to far off Cathay!

The blue waters of Mer Douce, now ploughed by the
barques of commerce, has seen many a flotilla other than
those of trade! Ages ago the birch bark canoes of the
Indian tribes coasted its shores, in pursuit of hunting or
fishing, or descended in warlike fleets upon a tribal foe
in internecine strife. Later the white man came—the
voyageur, the courier-de-bois breasted its waves in birch
canoes, in search of peltry and of new lands; and later
still the trader crossed its bosom in York boats laden
with peltry from the Far North. And at a still later
time, its bosom has seen War! Red War! And
vessels have sailed its waters intent only on destruction;
but these times are now happily long past. Changes
many has it seen, but its blue tide flows on, to join the

mighty and majestic river which drains half a continent, to empty itself at last, past the cold bleak shores of Anticosti and Labrador, into the Western Ocean !

In the early days, Mer Douce teemed with fish—pike and pickerel and the lordly salmon trout, white fish and herrings teemed its waters in shoals. Over 90 years ago fishing stations were established amongst the fishing islands on the western shores of the present Bruce Peninsula. That shore was, in the early days, the scene of a great fishing business. Men from the south came with boats and nets and supplies and awaited the "run" of the shoal of fish. The advance of a "shoal of fish" was indicated by a wave of light advancing along the waters shorewards. Boats and nets were then gotten out, and nets and floats put in order and oars were vigorously plied to surround the "shoal" and prevent its escape.

This effected, the seine was dropped and its ends rowed towards the shore in separate boats, the fish glancing and leaping to avoid the snare, but all to no avail. The landing of the net brought to view a gleaming, glittering, flapping mass of fish—often thrown out with shovels, by the fishermen standing knee-deep in the water, on to the shore—to gasp their lives away. Another gang quickly slit the fish open, disembowelled and packed them in layers of salt for shipment to the south. The "run" was sometimes so great as to require several days to salt, pack and cure all the "catch."

At the time of the first settlement of Bruce the "shoals" of fish were still prodigious and the "runs" still extremely large.

In springtime the "shoals" of herring ascended the rivers and streams emptying on the eastern shore in

prodigious numbers to spawn, returning to the lake
after spawning. The Penetangore River in Kincardine
Township; the Sauble and Rankin Rivers in Arran
and Arnabel Townships; the Saugeen; the Pine, the
Eighteen Mile River in Huron; the Nine Mile River
in Kinloss; the Yokissippi in Greenock and Culross;
Willow Creek in Bruce Township, all had their tide
of herring, rushing in thousands to their spawning
grounds on the head waters of these streams.

The herring season was a great source of enjoyment
and profit to the early settlers. Parties of neighbours
joined together to go to the lake and spear, net, or
pitchfork the herring on to the shore for their supply of
fish food for the following winter.

One bright spring morning, the Beaumonts,
Neubeckers and Gordon families set out for the lake, in
wagons, for fish. The route pursued was the Durham
Line through to the village of Penetangore on Lake
Huron. In the Beaumont wagon were Guy driving,
with Alex and Jack, Mrs. Beaumont and Alice, and with
supplies of food and tents and bedding for camping out
for a couple of days at the fishing. There were also
blankets, cooking utensils and tubs for the fish. All
the wagons headed for the Penetangore River. Arriving at Sutton's Hollow, on the outskirts of Penetangore
village, on the evening of the first day, they
made their different camps in the valley—the Gordons
and Neubeckers hard by.

The building of the different camps completed, the
tents erected, the fuel gathered, and camp fires built and
supper partaken of, everybody gathered at Beaumont's
camp to spend the evening—Mrs. Gordon, George and
Harry Gordon and their sister Mary and Stephen
Neubecker. With songs and jokes the evening passed

pleasantly away and all retired to their camps at an early hour to get needed rest, for the morrow would be a busy day at the fish. Next morning the work began in earnest. Nets and spears were gotten out and put in order and the young men proceeded to the river with them.

The nets were set in the shallower parts of the stream, and leaving two men to watch them the others proceeded up stream for a quarter of a mile and then began wading the river downwards, slapping the water with their spears and with long poles and raising a commotion in order to drive the fish downstream towards the nets.

On approaching the nets they were found well filled with herring and were then drawn ashore and the fish removed from the nets, where all hands turned to and cut open the fish, salted and packed them in tubs and bags for transport to the camps and later in the wagons to the homesteads.

In the afternoon nets were set afresh in a part of the river higher up stream, and while some of the young men went farther up to drive down the fish to the nets, others took spears to try a different sport. Amongst these latter was George Gordon, who travelling up stream to a quiet reach of the river, discovered a large shoal of fish, and succeeded in spearing one of the largest—a 10 lb. salmon trout. This he carried to camp with the intention of presenting it to Miss Alice Beaumont.

On approaching the Beaumont Camp, George was accosted by Mrs. Beaumont.

" Why George! Where did you get the big fish? Isn't it a beauty!"

" Yes, I speared it up the river!" said George " and brought it here, to give to Miss Alice! Where is she?"

" She went down the river about half an hour ago to gather flowers. I am sure she will be delighted with your present," said the mother.

After inquiring the direction in which she had gone, George deposited the fish on Mrs. Beaumont's table, and then started for the river.

The Penetangore River, at this point, runs through a valley about a quarter-mile in width, whose surface was covered with cedar, tamarac and balsams. Through these George forced his way, until he came to the River bank. On looking up and down he was unable to find any trace of the girl. With some misgivings he followed the left bank of the river down stream and presently came to an open glade which extended back on each side of the river. The river here ran deeply but was not of wide extent. Upon its farther or northern bank the glade was covered with wild daffodils, now in their deepest yellow, whilst across the river at this point an elm tree had fallen from the southern shore, in such a manner that its lower half lay upon the water and the other end touched the northern bank.

On looking at this natural bridge, George was horrified to see Alice Beaumont's head lying against the log, in the middle of the stream, and with her arm thrown across and clinging to it and her body submerged in the river.

With a cry of " Alice !" George bounded to the tree and began running rapidly across the fallen elm to the helpless girl. Grasping her arms he drew her upwards on to the fallen tree, and then carrying her dripping form to the shore, laid her tenderly upon the river bank. With pale face and closed eyes she remained motionless —she had fainted. George thought her dead and called again and again.

"Alice! Alice! Speak to me! Say you are not dead!" and sitting down he took the girl's head in his lap and began chafing the temples and hands and continuing his cries, and in his frenzy kissed the cold lips and called her his love.

Presently Alice opened her eyes and seeing George blushed and attempted to rise. Now the lover had another transport of joy that the object of his affection was not dead. "Oh! I'm so glad, Alice, that you can speak! Do not attempt to get up! Rest until your strength returns! How! Oh how did it happen?" inquired George.

"I am strong enough now to sit up and tell you George!" declared the girl, and suiting the action to the word, sat up.

"I came down to the river for flowers—you know they are beginning to awaken in the woods! I saw those beautiful daffodils on the other shore and felt sure I could easily walk across the fallen tree and get them, but somehow, when I reached the centre of the river, the flowing water made me dizzy and the next I knew I was in the river and grasping the log. You know I cannot swim, and oh, it seemed an age before anyone would come! I tried several times to climb on to the log but my hands would always slip and my water-soaked garments prevented, and I had at last made up my mind to die!" and the girl shuddered.

On this George placed his arm about her for support and with a sympathetic voice said "Well, it's all over now, Alice! Don't think about it any more! But there's something I want to ask you!" and he endeavoured to catch her eye, but Miss Alice evidently had a premonition of what was coming and turned her face away.

"Alice, did you hear what I said as you came out

of your faint?'' said George. The girl turned her head away but made no answer.

"There is no use in me beating about the bush, Alice dear—you must have long known I love you dearly!" said George. "Can you care for me, Alice?"

The girl still made no reply but began softly crying. "Oh! Alice I will not say another word if it hurts you to hear me declare what I have. Can you never care for me?" and George gazed with his soul in his eyes at the woman whom he loved so deeply. At this Alice sobbed more deeply, swaying as she did so and George put his arm around her, when her head came gently to rest upon his shoulder, while her sobs still continued. That was her woman's answer. George kissed her and fondled her; called her his Life and Hope and "sweetheart" and presently her sobbing ceased and they engaged in love's sweet nothings. Presently George bethought him of her wet clothes. "Oh! "Oh! What a dolt I am! You will get a chill and your death from cold! Come back to the camp at once and change to dry clothes!" he said

Alice lifted her face from his shoulder, rosy with blushes. "I'm not a bit cold! Still I must be a sight in these wet clothes!"

A true daughter of Eve her first thought was as to her appearance. She—like every woman—wished to look her best in the eyes of her lover.

George lifted her to her feet and drawing her to him, raised her face to his, and kissing her on the lips said, "Now sweetheart, all my troubles and misgivings are over. From now on my aim in life will be to make you happy!"

Taking her arm he assisted her through the glade and then back through the undergrowth of cedars until they arrived at Beaumont's Camp.

On reaching camp, Mrs. Beaumont, who had been busily preparing the dinner, on seeing the bedraggled appearance of her daughter, looked sharply at the young people and then evidently well satisfied at what she saw, bundled Miss Alice into the tent for a change into dry clothing.

George then recounted to Mrs. Beaumont the accident which had occurred to Alice on attempting to cross the river on the log, how he had rescued her, and of the declaration he had made to her, and that she had accepted him. This was grateful news to Mrs. Beaumont, who had always had a very high opinion of George Gordon and had always secretly hoped these two young people would come together.

Presently Miss Alice emerged from the tent with dry clothing, her face a rosy red from blushes.

"Well! I'm glad you two have settled your affairs between you. But you can't take Alice away from me at once, George Gordon! I cannot get along without her this summer! Mary and I cannot yet manage alone!" said Mrs. Beaumont, casting an anxious glance at the young couple.

Alice again blushed a rosy red. "Oh! Mother I'm not going to leave you! You are the best mother in the world and I'll never leave you!" cried the embarrassed girl, and going up to the mother she threw her arms around her neck.

"Hoighty! Toighty! What is this? Of course you'll leave me when the proper time comes!" exclaimed Mrs. Beaumont, "we'll have no sickly sentimentality about the matter. You are to go with your man and marry him, but only after a reasonable interval!" declared the now aroused matron.

George Gordon had stood an interested spectator during this colloquy. He now spoke up. "All

right! Mother! I will be content to wait any reasonable time for Alice."

"Yes indeed you will! I can assure you of that.
You can't have her before next spring! There's so
much to do and such a short time to do it in!" replied
Mrs. Beaumont.

"All right, Mother! Whatever you say we will
do!" returned George, and going up to Miss Alice,
planted another kiss on her lips, whereat the blushes
came rosier than ever on her face.

"Well! I declare!" exclaimed Mrs. Beaumont on
viewing this. "Modesty is not one of your failings,
Mr. George Gordon!"

"Well! but Mother, Alice now belongs to me and
right of ownership gives me the right to kiss her! Is
that not so?" and George viewed the mother with a
twinkle in his eye.

"Go along with you! I hope you will think as
much of her five years from now as you do at present!
And another thing you mustn't come to visit her too
often—not more than once a week—once a week is about
all the 'spooning' I can bear to see!" declared Mrs.
Beaumont.

Preparations then went forward for breaking camp
and returning to Brant. The "catch" of fish on both
days had been tremendous. Every tub, bag and utensil
of every kind in each camp had been filled to over-
flowing with the abundant herring. These had first
been gutted and packed in layers of salt for preservation.

By mid-afternoon the camps had been struck—fires
extinguished—the wagons loaded with the camp para-
phernalia as well as the fish; the oxen inspanned, and
the fishers started the homeward trek over the Durham
Road for their homes.

CHAPTER XXVII.

The Murder.

In the early days before railroads came to the "Bush" the settler had to drive long distances to dispose of his grain. Before gravel roads were introduced into the country, the roadways were mostly quagmires during spring and fall and part of the summer, and only after the first frost and snow set in could the teaming of wheat to the nearest point on the railways be undertaken.

After the Elora Road was opened, the most of the grain went to Guelph, where it was shipped out on the Grand Trunk Railway; but before this shipping point was available the nearest R.R. points to Western Brant were Goderich, the northern terminus of the Buffalo and Lake Huron Railway, and Seaforth and Clinton upon the same railway, and somewhat nearer and further to the east.

When winter set in long strings of loaded teams were seen upon the highways leading to these railroad towns. The chief route for these was southward from Western Brant, following the boundary road between Carrick and Culross Townships, through Formosa and Ambleside to Belmore, and thence still southwards on the boundary between Howick and Turnberry Townships in Huron County, until the boundary of Grey Township in the same County was reached, where a jog of a mile to the westwards brought the teamster to the boundary of Morris and Grey Townships, and thence south 12 miles brought him to the boundary of McKillip Township, and a 10-mile stretch across this landed him in Seaforth and at the railroad.

The settlers in Greenock Township, and particularly its western part, took the Durham Line to Penetangore or Kincardine, from whence the Goderich Road led them to the railroad, 30 miles away.

The following winter Stephen Neubecker had made several trips with wheat to Seaforth, and now towards the end of February was making his final delivery of grain to that point. That load would finish all the surplus grain his father—old Philip Neubecker—had to sell.

Old Sol was rising higher in the heavens every day, and his attacks upon the snow-covered " bush " roads were daily becoming more vigorous. On his previous trip one of Stephen's brothers had accompanied him, but on this last trip he was alone.

He had left home at an early hour on a Friday morning with his team and load of wheat, had gained the boundary to the westwards by daylight, and passing through Formosa and Ambleside, had reached Chambers Tavern in Belmore by 9 o'clock in the morning. Here after watering his horses, he hurried on in an effort to reach Brussels—18 miles away to the southward—by noon for a rest and feed for his animals.

Brussels was reached by 1 o'clock, and outspanning, Stephen fed his horses and gave them an hour's rest while he took his own dinner at the tavern.

At 2 p.m. he again inspanned and took the road, expecting to reach Seaforth that night. After leaving Brussels his road still led southward, and with Seaforth 18 miles away. Although the horses did not get off a walk and the sleigh was heavily loaded, it was shortly after 6 o'clock when he reached the Queen's Hotel, Seaforth, and put up 'or the night. Stabling his team and procuring some supper he retired to bed, anxious to make an early sale on the market the next morning.

Early the next day, after breakfasting, he drove his load of grain on to the market and quickly made a sale. Shortly he prepared to leave for home, expecting to reach there by night. This he could do, as the sleighing was good—the empty sleigh was no load at all for his horses.

After making a few purchases for his home folks he settled his "bill" at the hotel "bar," and hitching up his team struck out for the north and home.

The day was mild for the time of year and the snow thawing fast, so much so that in spots on the road the earth showed through. Steve met many loaded sleighs going south with grain to the railroad, and he overtook many empty sleighs returning homewards. These often formed long strings of vehicles, from which individual parts broke off here and there as different roads in different townships were reached. One o'clock found him again at Brussels, where the horses were stabled and fed and he himself procured his dinner. After an hour and a half's rest the journey was resumed, but night was falling as he passed through Howick. With the disappearance of the sun the air became much colder, and by darkness the cold became intense— evidently below zero weather. Presently Steve became chilled, so jumping off the sleigh he walked along behind to improve the circulation and bring some heat to his numbed members and chilled body; and presently being warmed, again took his seat in the sleigh. Shortly after doing so, and being but a short distance south of Belmore, he descried the figure of a man using a heavy walking stick and travelling northward ahead of him and upon the sleigh track. On overhauling the pedestrian Steve invited him to take a " ride." The traveller accepted the offer and, jumping on the sleigh, sat down upon the board seat beside Steve.

" Are you travelling far ?" asked Steve.

" Going to Formosa !" replied the man, turning his face to Steve, and from which the strong odour of whisky emanated.

" Why, it's Jack Haag !" cried Steve. " What are you doing down here, Jack ?"

" I am on my own business !" surlily replied Haag. Steve saw that the man was in liquor, and as they were in a lonely piece of road decided to humour him.

" Well, of course, every man's business is his own. I meant no offence. I've been down to Seaforth with a load of wheat and sold it well, and am taking the money home to father," replied Steve, and clapped his hand to his breast.

" That so ?" said Haag. " I'd heard from Guy Beaumont you'd gone down with wheat and thought I'd meet you. You and Alice Beaumont are pretty ' thick,' aren't you ?"

" Now, Jack, drop that subject, or we are sure to quarrel. You harped on that subject once before, and you know what came of it," replied Steve.

" I can lick any Neubecker or Gordon that ever lived, and as for that hussy, Alice Beaumont, I will yet make her pride have a fall !" declared Haag.

Steve immediately stopped the team and, rising to his feet, cried out : " Haag, get off my sleigh ! You are not fit to ride with decent people. No team of mine will ever haul a slanderer of Alice Beaumont. Git !" and he gave Haag—who in the meantime also had risen to his feet—a shove towards the side of the sleigh. The latter with a curse whirled, and bringing the heavy walking stick down with crushing force upon Neubecker's head, stretched him senseless in the bottom of the sleigh.

"Ah! you b----r! You'd play high and mighty with me, would you, and for that hussy's sake?" cried Haag, as with vicious oaths he brought the stick down again and again upon Stephen's unprotected head. The latter lay as dead. The team had meanwhile remained standing.

The quarrel and its results appeared to sober Haag, who now in the gloaming peered up and down the road to see if there were any observers of what had happened. But nothing was in sight. At that date it was a lonely stretch of country betwixt Belmore and Formosa.

Bending down, Haag carefully searched Neubecker's pockets, and finally, pinned to an inside pocket of the vest, he found the wheat money—a package of bank bills. These he appropriated to his own use by shoving them into the various pockets, and then dismounting from the sleigh, he gave the off-horse a resounding whack upon the haunches with his walking stick, and stood in the snow of the roadway watching the galloping horses disappear in the distance, with poor Stephen Neubecker lying senseless in the bottom of the sleigh.

Standing there in the roadway in a brown study, the murderer continued gazing vacantly to the northwards long after the team had disappeared, evidently realizing that the mark of Cain was upon him, and wondering what his future should be.

Turning at length, he crossed the roadway and struck across the clearing to the eastwards and disappeared.

The night grew colder; the stars shone with a bright glitter in the sky. Now and then a crash rent the silent air as the softened ice, in pools by the roadside, contracted with a bang to the touch of the Frost King.

The team galloped on about a mile, and then terror-dissipated and with reeking coats, slowed down to a walk, their breath two columns of white steam driven from their nostrils. The silent form still lay in the bottom of the sleigh where it had been struck down; only a stream of blood trickled from the half-opened mouth on to the wheat straw littering the bottom of the sleigh.

Poor Stephen! For this he had gone through 26 years of the hard life of a pioneer. For all his good nature, his kindness to the helpless, his upright life, his disappointed hopes in a marital future, he had come to this, to be stricken down like a beast at almost the Doorway of Life and the beginning of Manhood! Such is Life! Such is fortune, and such is Fate!

The five miles separating Howick from Belmore were dreary in the extreme—the roadway stretched away to the north with almost unbroken forest on either hand. No team, no soul of any kind, showed upon its white surface that night. At times the team of horses almost slowed to a halt, but, chilled with the biting, freezing air, moved on again. Owing to this fact it was almost 10 o'clock at night before the team reached the hill on the south of the valley in which the village of Belmore stands. Slowly descending this and coming to John Chambers's tavern, the team turned into the driving shed adjoining the stables, and there stood throughout the night, no doubt wondering what had become of their hitherto kind driver, Stephen Neubecker.

And poor Stephen? He still lay, an inert form, in

the bottom of the sleigh.   The blood from the mouth had now stopped flowing, but had formed a pool in the bottom of the sleigh and had become congealed.

The left jaw-bone had been broken by Haag's blow, and one poor eye—the left—had been smashed and had partly protruded from the socket.   The left side of the skull also had been smashed.

Through the long cold hours of the night the silent form still lay where it had been stricken.   The poor horses, chilled with the cold, kept stamping their feet and shifting their position from time to time, but as the driving shed floor was of earth no sound of this reached the inmates of the adjoining tavern.

As it was a Sunday morning the hotel slept late.   At 8 o'clock next morning John Chambers, tavern keeper, threw open the front door to see what the weather was like.   On looking out, he beheld part of a sleigh projecting from the driving shed, and putting on his cap, advanced to see whose team it was.   On reaching the sleigh he perceived the form of a man lying on the bottom, and shouted:

" Having a sleep, old man?   Better come into the ' bar ' and get warm."

Advancing to shake the man, whom he deemed sleeping, he perceived the pool of congealed blood, and then hastily turning the body over, discovered the mangled face.

" My God!   My God!   What is this?" exclaimed Chambers.   " Is it an accident or is it murder?   Hey, Tony!" he shouted across to Anthony Messner, who was at the doorway of his own house, " come over here.   Here is a man who has been killed."   Messner ran across the road and looked at the injured man.

" Why, it's Stephen Neubecker of Western Brant !" he exclaimed. " How did he come here ?"

" I don't know," said Chambers. " I only just discovered the sleigh on opening the tavern door a few minutes ago, and walked over here to see who owned the team. Is he dead, do you think ?"

" I don't know. I think I can detect a faint heart-beat," declared Messner, running his hand under the victim's shirt over the heart.

" Yes, I'm sure he's alive. I can feel a faint pulse. Let us carry him into the tavern."

The alarm quickly spread through the village, and soon the driving shed around the sleigh was filled with people. Stephen was tenderly carried into the tavern and placed on a bed in a warm room. Warm water and soft cloths were quickly brought, and Mrs. Chambers tenderly washed the the broken face and replaced as much as possible the destroyed eye. The hands and feet of the victim were found badly frozen, and from this fact the tavern keeper deduced the body had lain in the sleigh during the night, and as he was certain there was no team nor sleigh in his driving shed when he locked up his hotel for the previous night, the injuries must have been received at some point on the road to the south.

On calling Anthony Messner to one side and pointing this out, the latter said : " Yes, the sleigh track in the snow entering the driving shed showed it came from the south."

" I think, Tony, we should start out at once before any teams get on the road to destroy the signs, and we may be able to discover how he came by his injuries," said Chambers.

" Yes, I think it would be wise," rejoined Messner.

Chambers hurried off to the stables, where he hitched up his horse and rough "jumper," and throwing in some robes and blankets, hastily drove up to the hotel, where Messner joined him.

In the meantime Mrs. Chambers kept bathing the injured man's face, while some kind neighbours used snow and friction upon the frozen hands and feet. After about half an hour of this Neubecker's breathing became audible. "See!" cried Mrs. Karter, "he is breathing. He is not dead! The poor man! How did he come by these awful injuries? His breath does not smell of liquor."

Messner and the tavern-keeper drove southward towards Howick upon the boundary road and kept a sharp watch upon the roadway ahead. Nothing was seen of note until they had gone about 3 miles south of Belmore, when Messner suddenly exclaimed: "Stop! there are blood-stains upon the snow between the sleigh tracks!" Chambers pulled up, and Messner hastily got out and made a minute survey of the blood-stains. The stains showed vividly upon the white snow, were of about the size of cherries, and were about two feet apart.

Getting on to the jumper again, they followed the blood-stains southward until about half a mile south, where they ended in a large blood-stain in the centre of the road.

"Stop, John! We must go carefully now so as not to obliterate any suspicious traces. Here is where Neubecker met with his injuries. Let us piece the evidence together and, if possible, find out what caused them," said Messner.

Messner then dismounted from the jumper a good 20 feet from the large blood-stain upon the road, and walking very carefully in the unbroken snow upon the west side of the road, carefully and minutely scrutinized the roadway. "A team stood here for a time," he said. "There you can see the marks of the shoes where the horses stamped into the snow, and there are footmarks leading off the road to the left and across yonder field. John, there's been foul play here!" said Messner, addressing the tavern keeper. "Do you go on to Ambleside and wait there at the hotel for me. I am going to follow these footmarks across the fields. There has been murder done here!" and taking out his store-keeper's tape line he made careful measurements of the footmarks, jotting down the measurements in a note-book.

Chambers accordingly drove on to the British Hotel at Ambleside, while Messner crossed the roadway fence and followed the footmarks across an adjacent 10-acre clearing.

The footmarks were those of an adult man and were of fairly large size. After following them halfway across the clearing, he found them running in the direction of a log shanty on the edge of the clearing belonging to a settler named George Grimm.

Following along the footmarks he arrived at the settler's shanty, from which a collie dog rushed at him, but was called off by the owner, who, coming to the door, accosted him.

"Good day, Tony. Come to visit me?"

"Hello, Grimm!" cried Messner. "Call your dog off and come out here. I wish to show you something." Driving the dog into an outhouse, Grimm, a man of about 40 years, joined Messner, who, taking him back into the field, pointed out the footmarks he had followed, saying, "Do you know who made those footmarks, George?" and at the same time viewing the marks made by Grimm's shoes in the snow; but a glance told him they were unlike.

" No, I don't," said Grimm.

" There was an attempt made at murder out there on the roadway last night," replied Messner, pointing over at the road. " The victim is lying at Chambers's tavern in Belmore at the point of death, and the man who did it produced those traces you see there," and he pointed down at the footmarks.

" So! Mein Gott was a Welt! Why, a stranger —a man I never saw before—came to my shanty last night about 8 o'clock and asked for supper. Said he was on his way to Teeswater !" declared Grimm.

" Describe his appearance, George," said Messner.

" He had black hair and eyes, and had a black moustache, and would be about my height, and I would say about 24 or 26 years of age," replied Grimm.

" So! and what became of him ?" inquired Messner. " Where is he now ?"

" Ich weis nicht !" (I don't know.) " After he ate his supper he did not stay, but pulled out a large roll of bank bills to pay for his meal, but I told him we never took pay for food, and he left. He said he had to be going and mentioned Teeswater, so I supposed he went there. He left about 9 o'clock," declared Grimm.

" In what direction ?" inquired Messner.

" I don't know," answered Grimm, " but we can find out by his footmarks, as none of my family have been out of the house to-day."

On going outside the two men quickly found the footmarks similar to those of Messner had followed across the 10-acre clearing in the direction of the woods eastwards of Grimm's stable. Following up these traces, they presently came out on the farm of a man named Anthony Miller. The footmarks entered Miller's clearing and ran in the direction of Miller's shanty. Arriving here, their advance heralded by the clamour of dogs, which every settler kept, the door of the shanty opened, and Anthony Miller came out.

" Hello, Tony!" he cried. " You are out hunting early, and where is your gun?" addressing Tony Messner, who, because of his business as store keeper, all the settlers of the neighbourhood knew.

" I am out hunting, but not the sort of game you suppose," replied Messner.

" Did you have a young man about 26 years of age, with black eyes and moustache, here yesterday evening between 9 and 10 o'clock at night?" inquired the store keeper. The settler hesitated, and then said:

" Why do you ask?"

" Well, a murder was done over on the boundary road last night, and everything points to the man I've described as being the murderer," said Messner. "Was the man here?"

" Yes, he was here, but did not remain very long. I don't know where he went to," declared Miller.

Messner and Grimm then went into Miller's shanty, but found no one except the settler's family. They examined the surroundings of the shanty, and found the footmarks leading down to the side road and from which they could be traced to the concession line, in which they were lost, but whether the fugitive had directed his course to the westwards, Teeswater and the Lake, or eastwards towards Mildmay and the Elora Line, for escape by the latter to Guelph, they could not tell.

Reluctantly they returned to Miller's shanty, from whence Messner walked to Belmore, where he joined Chambers.

CHAPTER XXVIII.

TRACING THE FUGITIVE.

On reaching Belmore, they found the poor victim—Stephen Neubecker—still alive but in a muttering delirium. Kind hands had made him as comfortable as it was possible in the crude surroundings of a log tavern. Mrs. Chambers and her maidservants Hannah Day and Madeline Batty, after bathing the injured head, had bound it up and a bandage had been placed around the broken jaw. Nourishment—milk and whisky—had been forced teaspoonful wise between the teeth and with painful efforts—because of the broken mandible—it had been swallowed.

Messner now bent over the broken man and called to him. "Stephen, don't you know me?" The right eye of the injured man turned towards him— the light of reason seemed to flicker for an instant therein but the only answer was "hawk! hawk!" muttering which, the injured man turned away his head. "He is not in his right mind!" said John Chambers. "He does not understand what you are saying to him!"

"Yes! It seems so!" replied Messner. "I think we should send to Walker's Settlement for Dr. Kay, who is also a Coroner and can investigate this matter!"

Accordingly Chambers again hitched up his horse and dispatched a messenger to the Clay Banks for the Doctor, and acquainting him with the manner in which Neubecker had been found and also of his injuries.

About mid-afternoon Dr. Kay, the Coroner, accompanied by another man, Michael Laborde, County Constable, drove up in a cutter and entered the tavern. The doctor made a minute examination of the patient and found the left lower jaw bone fractured so that a pointed portion of the broken bone projected into the mouth and that the left orbital cavity had been smashed in and with it the left eye burst open, destroying the sight; also that the hands and feet were badly frozen.

During this examination, Neubecker had kept up a continual muttering the only intelligible word of which sounded like " Hawk! Hawk!" as if he were endeavouring to clear his throat.

" He has been muttering that way since early morning, Doctor!" declared the tavern keeper, Chambers.

" When and where was he found?" demanded Dr. Kay.   Chambers and Messner then acquainted him with the circumstances of the finding of Neubecker and what they had already done in an effort to find by what means his injuries had been come by. Messner described his visits to Grimm's and Miller's shanties and that a stranger whose tracks led thereto from the blood-stained road had been in both places the night before but had left early that morning for an unknown destination.

Laborde, who was a County Constable, now asked " Did either Grimm or Miller know the man?"   " I do not know!" replied Messner.   " I do not remember asking Miller directly if he knew the man or not, but Grimm declared he was a stranger and that he had never seen the man before!"

" I think we had better investigate that part again," said the Constable.

" Will you go along with me, Mr. Messner, to

Grimm's and Miller's shanties and help me clear this matter up?"

Mr. Messner readily gave his consent and taking a fresh horse, he and the constable departed south on the boundary road. After travelling about three miles Messner exclaimed :

"Now about here I saw the first blood-stain this morning and they continued down beyond that swamp ahead there where the large blood-stains are located and where the injuries to Neubecker must have occurred!"

"So?" exclaimed Laborde. They drove rapidly on and presently reaching the large blood-stains on the road Laborde dismounted and examined them and the surroundings minutely. He noticed footmarks in the snow leading across the neighbouring fields.

"Those on the right are my footmarks!" declared Messner. "Those on the left belong to the stranger, whom I traced this morning!"

"All right!" said the Constable. "I'm going over to Grimm's and Miller's to investigate. You say Miller's land abuts on to Grimm's but on the other side-road? Very well, you drive down to Belmore. I shall go down the side-road from Miller's to the Concession and meet you at the Belmore Hotel in a couple of hours!"

Messner acccordingly drove off, while the Constable crossing the road fence, followed the footmarks carefully across the fields. Now and again stopping where the snow was thin and the outline of the boots very distinct. Then pulling out paper, pencil and rule he made a series of minute measurements of the boot, sole and heel—width, length, and thickness of sole, which he jotted down on a piece of paper.

Presently he approached Grimm's shanty, out of

which the owner, who had evidently observed the Constable's actions, emerged.

"Are you Charles Grimm?" asked the Constable. "Yes!" replied Grimm.

"Well, I'm Michael Laborde, Constable for the County of Bruce! A murder was done on the road down there last night and I'm here to ask what you know about the man who ate his supper at your house last night!" said Laborde.

Grimm then related all he knew about the stranger— the time of his arrival; his appearance, his desire to press on his journey, etc.

"And did you not know the man?" asked Laborde. "No! I never set eyes on him before last night!" declared the farmer looking full in Laborde's face.

After some further queries the Constable left and circling the logbarn again took up the fugitive's trail through the woods and across the "blind line" as the line was called marking the junction of two abutting lots, and presently entered Anthony Miller's clearing.

As he neared the shanty of the latter, the clamor of the dogs, as in the morning, brought Anthony Miller to the door. On reaching the doorway Laborde cried:

"Good-day! Are you Anthony Miller?"

"Yes! That is my name," said Miller. "What is it that you want?"

"Well!" answered the Constable, "not very much! Only a little information. You had a man—a stranger —stop at your house last night. What time did he arrive and what time did he leave?"

"I think that is my private affair, and no one's business but my own!" hotly replied Miller.

"See here! My man! Don't take up that line of talk or you will get yourself in trouble. A murder was committed on the roadway in front of Charles Grimm's lot last night and the murderer was in both Grimm's and your house. My name is Laborde. I'm a County Constable investigating this matter and if you refuse to answer my questions I will have a warrant sworn out for your arrest, when you will be compelled to answer! Now what are you going to do!" exclaimed the Constable.

"Well! there was a man came here last night and asked to stay the night—-I gave him a bed, but he was up and away before daylight this morning!" answered Miller.

"Where did he go?" asked Laborde.

"I do not know! He didn't say!" returned Miller.

"Describe his appearance?" said the Constable. Miller described the stranger's appearance, giving the same description as had Charles Grimm. "Now look into my face, Miller! Did you know the man?" asked the Constable.

Miller had looked at the Constable, but on hearing the question turned his face away. "No! I did not know the man!" he said. Laborde looked at Miller intently for a minute and then turning to Mrs. Miller, who meantime had taken her stand by her husband's side, said:

"Your husband is taking a very unwise course, Mrs. Miller. He is aiding and abetting an escaping murderer to flee from Justice. He is not telling me the truth. He knows who the murderer is. Do you want to have your husband thrown into jail and tried for his life as an accomplice of the murderer of Stephen Neubecker of Brant?" asked the Constable of the now terrified woman.

"Oh! Tony! If you know tell the Constable the name of the man! What will become of us if you are thrown into jail?" and the woman gathered her apron to her face and began sobbing.

" Well ! I did not know a murder had been committed and he asked me not to mention his name !" said Miller.

" Who was he ?" cried Laborde.

" It was Jack Haag of Brant !' answered the farmer.

" Jack Haag of Brant !" repeated the Constable. " My God—Stephen Neubecker's neighbour. This was not done for robbery ! The cause lay deeper !" and the Constable turned musingly away. After a time he asked :

" In which direction did Haag leave ?"—" I do not know, when I got up this morning he was gone. Evidently he went down to the side road, but from there I don't know which way he went !" declared the now harassed man.

Laborde mused aloud.

" He has either gone to the west, in an endeavour to reach the lake shore, Goderich and the railroad, or east to Mernersville and the Elora Road to escape by Guelph ! Now which ? He mentioned Teeswater to Grimm but that may have been a blind ! Well I must be off ! Good day !" This last to Miller as Laborde departed for Belmore.

Reaching Belmore he acquainted Anthony Messner with what he had learned. " Well ! I formed the same opinion this morning, that Miller was concealing something from me !" exclaimed Messner. " And so Jack Haag is the murderer ? I have often seen him in my store in Belmore, but never thought he would commit a murder. He was a drinking man. Drink has probably brought him to this !" declared Messner.

" Well ! It may have been but I've another theory, with which drink has nothing to do !" replied Laborde.

" So ? What is that ?" asked Messner.

" Jealousy !" curtly replied the Constable.

" Jealousy !" exclaimed Messner, " How ?"

" Why Haag was jealous of Stephen Neubecker because he thought Miss Alice Beaumont favoured Neubecker's suit and not his own !" answered Laborde.

" So !" said the astonished Messner. " What a world ! What a world ! And so that was how the ' wind blew ' !"

" Yes ! I lived near them for some time in Brant and knew there was continual jealousy because of that matter !" declared Laborde.

" Now we must be getting back to Walker's Settlement," declared the Constable.

Getting out their horse they quickly drove back there, which they reached by dark and the constable then told what he had learned at Miller's shanty.

At Belmore, Dr. Kay, after succeeding in administering some medicine to the victim, had left for his home, leaving instructions to keep the cold cloths applied to the injured head of the victim, and that he would visit the patient on the following day. The muttering delirium still kept up, " Hawk ! Hawk !" resounding continually through the room.

" Ah ! Now I understand !" said John Chambers. " It is ' Haag ! Haag !' that he is trying to say. He is trying to give the name of the man who beat him !"

" Yes ! Yes !" said Laborde, " there is now no doubt about that. We must endeavour to head off the murderer before he gets out to the ' front ' (as the older settled parts of the Province were then called) and escape to the United States. But he's had a day's start and according to Grimm is well supplied with money !"

" I wonder !" and the Constable paused, and then hurrying into the adjoining room where poor Stephen lay he made a rapid and thorough search of Neubecker's clothing, but found no money. Turning to John Chambers he said, " It is as I thought. Haag attempted to murder Steve and then robbed him. Steve must have been to Clinton or Seaforth with a load of wheat and was returning home when attacked. He would have the wheat money on his person !"

" What a devil that Haag must be !" exclaimed the tavern keeper.

" Well !" said the Constable, " I must get away to Brant and see Neubecker's people. I want you to send a man with a rig and take me to Walker's Settlement to-night. To-morrow I will go out to Neubecker's farm and make inquiries," and so saying the Constable left.

Next morning Steve was no better. He still kept up an almost continual muttering, dozing for short intervals. Some nourishment had been gotten down his throat. The second day he sank visibly, so that by mid-afternoon when Dr. Kay arrived, it was plain that death was not far off.

The medical man after a short examination shook his head and said " his injuries are too great, and on top of that the exposure through the bitter night lying out in the driving shed has been the straw that is making the difference between life and death !" Steve's mutterings became less and less distinct and finally ceased altogether— then the breathing became more and more embarrassed and finally about dusk ceased altogether. After an interval it was resumed again—a smile appeared on the dying man's face—mangled though it was—he raised his battered head from the pillow and muttering one word " Alice " fell back dead !

The next day the hue and cry spread through Bruce : " Stephen Neubecker had been murdered by Jack Haag and the latter was a fugitive from justice !"

Michael Laborde at that time was a man of 45 years, stoutly and compactly built; a man of incisive speech, of a keen deductive and inquiring mind; well fitted mentally to pursue criminals, a " bloodhound of the law." Later on bringing Haag to justice he acquired the nickname of " Gallow's Mike." He now set out to exert all his powers in tracing the murderer and bringing him to the bar of justice.

Journeying out to old Philip Neubecker's farm the day thereafter he imparted the sad news of Stephen's death and learned all the particulars of that last fatal trip with the wheat to Seaforth!

And now the country was aroused! Its fair fame had been dragged in the mud by a brutal murder—the first in the annals of the " Bush." No effort nor expense was spared to bring the murderer to justice and a swift and condign punishment. Handbills were gotten out and scattered far and wide giving a full description of the murderer and offering a generous reward for his apprehension. Frontier points into Michigan and New York States were notified by telegraph—with a description—to be on the look-out for Haag—but it all came to nothing. The Hunted—for a time—escaped the Hunters.

And what of Haag? His short sleep at Anthony Miller's on the night of the murder had sobered him. He then realized to the full his perilous position. With the Mark of Cain upon him, he knew that in future his life would be a hunted one—that every man's hand would be against him and that he would be hunted like a wild beast to its lair. Revolving these things in his mind, he decided he would go to Michigan. His father had a brother, Casper Haag, residing near Bridgeport, a small town near Saginaw, Michigan. The problem was " how to reach there in safety." He decided to travel as much as possible by night, avoiding villages and towns, and that his best course would be to strike east and south and so avoid the travelled wheat roads to the west.

Accordingly he left Miller's before daybreak on that Sunday morning and travelling eastwards, came within a mile of Mernersville (Mildmay), which he avoided by taking the first side-road to the south—coming out on the Elora Road. Thence pursuing his way south, he passed through Balaclava before 7 o'clock in the morning. As it was a Sunday morning and everybody slept late he saw no people about the houses. Pursuing his way 6 miles farther he came in sight of Clifford. This he avoided by keeping to the boundary of Howick and Minto Townships, to the first concession south, where, turning to the left, brought him again after a mile of travel on to the Elora Road at John Weber's tavern (Butcher Jack), 1½ miles below Clifford. This place he reached by noon, and being tired and hungry, decided he would stop for dinner. To the tavern keeper he said he came from Mount Forest and had been into the western part of Howick Township to view some wild lands that were for sale but that none suited him and he was now getting back home.

After a hasty dinner—for he realized the necessity of putting as many miles as possible between himself and the scene of his crime—he again took to the road, and, travelling rapidly, came within sight of Harriston, which he avoided by making another detour, and then pursuing his way pressed on south-eastwards so that by dusk he was on the outskirts of Elora; and avoiding its Main Street, by skirting the west side of the town, passed on towards Guelph, which he finally reached about 9 o'clock worn and weary and haggard. Here he stopped at a small hotel on the north side of the town, securing quarters, and after some supper he retired to bed.

He was up next morning early and after breakfast and paying his bill at the bar he sought out a barber shop and had a haircut and shave, and had his heavy black moustache shaved off.

Some stores being by now opened, he visited one and secured an entire new suit of black broadcloth—replacing his own rough farm garments, a fine pair of shoes to replace the long cowhide boots, collar and tie and a " plug " or silk hat. Thus altered he had all the appearance of a smart business man. Hastily donning these garments in the back room of the store, he purchased a carpet bag, into which he stuffed his old clothes and boots. Thus equipped, he wended his way to the Grand Trunk Station, and ascertaining a passenger train would be going westwards in an hour, he waited.

With his changed appearance there was now little likelihood of his being recognized as the roughly clothed backwoodsman of the day before. He was confident that, because of the rapidity of his travelling, no word of his crime had yet gotten in advance of him. Of course there was yet the telegraph and the frontier, but he would go carefully there.

At 10 o'clock in the forenoon a passenger train from the east drew into the station and, boarding it openly, his journey to Michigan began. Passing through Berlin, Stratford, St. Mary's, Lucan, Ailsa Craig, Thedford, Camlachie, his train reached Pt. Edward on the Canadian side of the St. Clair River by 3 o'clock in the afternoon. Here the G.T.R. passenger coaches were carried across the river on a ferry. Haag knew that crossing the river would be the crucial time in his escape. If telegrams had already arrived from the north, then every passenger would be closely scrutinized and interrogated. Therefore he deemed it wise not to attempt it. Hiring a conveyance—a Democrat buggy, horse and driver at Point Edward Station, he said he wished to go to Sarnia, a mile away—as he lived there. Reaching Sarnia he went to an hotel, had supper and went to bed and laid awake for a couple of hours planning his next move. The next morning after breakfast he sauntered down to the waterfront and seeing a couple of fishermen overhauling their seines, asked them how the fishing was.

" Not too bad !" replied a young fisherman, " but it might be better !"

" Say ! What will you take to put me across to Port Huron ? I've a business matter to settle there and I'm in a hurry. The ferry only runs across when the trains come in from the east and that's too long to wait !"

" All right ! I'll run you across for $2.00 !" replied the fisherman.

" Done !" answered Haag. " Just wait a minute while I get a parcel which I have to take with me !" and hastily returning to the hotel, paid his bill and secured the valise with his old clothes, and reappeared at the water's side within a few minutes after leaving it. Throwing the valise into the boat, he followed. The fisherman cast off and raising a sail quickly passed out into the river. They were quickly in midstream when Haag raised the valise to his side, resting it on the thwart on which he sat. The boat careening to the breeze in midstream the valise plumped overboard, quickly sinking out of sight in the tumbling waters. " Oh ! my valise is overboard !" cried Haag.

" Too bad !" said the sailor, " you'll never see it again. The water here is 50 feet deep ! Too bad ! Too bad !" little knowing that Haag himself had given the valise a shove in order to destroy for good the evidence of the incriminating clothes.

The boat now made rapid progress towards the Michigan shore and presently drew into dock in Port Huron, on to which Haag quickly sprang and waving his hand in farewell to the ferryman, disappeared amongst the buildings of the town.

After wandering for some time up and down the streets of the town he sat down at length upon the doorstep of a deserted house and let his thoughts wander as they would.

His thoughts flew back to the old days and the old home back in Woolwich Township; the old log schoolhouse and his old playmate, fair-haired Stephen Neubecker, whom he had battered to death, and as he thought of that, a tear burst from his eyes and ran down his cheek and he resolved henceforth he would alter his mode of life—for he was now genuinely sorry for the past—change his name; live in some obscure place, and hope that time and remorse and an upright life would bring forgiveness! We shall see how he kept this resolve!

> "Playmates were we, little we thought it then,
>   How we should change when we should all be men.
> Ah! sweet boyhood days, free from all care and pain,
>   Playmates! Playmates! I wish we were boys again!"

CHAPTER XXIX.

THE ARREST.

PROVIDING himself with a warrant of arrest for murder, Laborde, on the following day, visited Gottlieb Haag's home. The news of what his son had done had not yet penetrated to that remote farmhouse. He inquired for Jack, saying he had some business to transact with him, but did not say what.

The old gray-haired father and mother welcomed him to their humble home, invited him to dinner, which meal they had just finished, but the constable declined, saying he had already dined.

He spoke of the outlook for spring, of the prospects of a good crop, judging by the amount of the past winter's snowfall, and kept the conversational ball rolling for some time until he satisfied himself Jack was not about the premises.

Then, taking another tack, he engaged old Gottlieb in reminiscences of his journey from Germany to Waterloo County, Canada, and his early life there before coming into the " Bush."

" And did you come across the Atlantic alone, Mr. Haag ?" he asked.

" No. There was my brother Casper and my sister Mary with me," replied the old man.

" And what became of them ? Where are they ?" inquired the Constable.

" Oh, Casper stayed ' down below ' in Waterloo for a couple of years, and then moved to Michigan, while my sister Mary married a man named Peter Schneider, and is still living in Waterloo County," replied the old man.

" Whereabouts ?" asked Laborde.

" Why, she's living in Wellesley Township close to Hawksville," replied Haag.

" And your brother Casper, whereabouts in Michigan is he ?" again inquired the Constable.

" He is farming near a place called Bridgeport, not very far from Saginaw, Michigan. I had a letter from him from there last summer. He asked me to send him my photograph and that of my family," replied the old man.

" You are quite a scattered family, Mr. Haag," observed the Constable.

Having now secured all the information he desired, the Constable took up another tack. " You should send your brother your photograph and that of your wife," he remarked.

" Yes, yes, I know. We had our photos taken last fall just before Christmas when we visited Berlin, but we are poor letter-writers and haven't sent it to Michigan yet," declared the old man.

" Won't you let me see it ?" asked Laborde.

" Oh, yes," cried Mrs. Haag, and rising and going to an inner room, she brought out a red plush-covered album, which she opened, disclosing a photo of the old couple—Mrs. Haag standing with her hand upon her husband's shoulder and old Gottlieb sitting. After praising the likeness, Laborde began idly turning the pages of the album, one photo showing the sister, Mrs.

Schneider, of Waterloo; one of their old Pastor, Rev. Helfirch, in Berlin; and then a striking likeness of Jack Haag.

"That is our son Jack! That picture was taken last fall, in Berlin, when ours was taken," declared Mrs. Haag.

"So!" said Laborde, and began turning the leaves to see the other photos, all the time keeping his finger on the photo of Jack Haag, which he managed surreptitiously to remove from its holder and secrete in his sleeve, and at the same time keeping up the conversation with the old couple.

Finally closing the album, he handed it to Mrs. Haag with the remark, "A very fine collection of photos, Mrs. Haag. Now I must be going. I'm sorry Jack is not at home. However, I will see him another time," and with this *double entendre* observation he left.

On his way back to Walker's he cogitated : "Now he has either gone to his sister in Wellesley Township or to the uncle in Michigan! Now which?" and he pondered the matter for some time. "Most likely to Michigan because it's outside of Canadian jurisdiction. Still, I will have to see Mrs. Schneider first."

Accordingly the next morning he set out on horseback from Walker's, and travelling southwards over the Elora Road reached Alma by mid-afternoon. He had stopped at Clifford and Harriston on his way south, and had made inquiries and exhibited the photograph, but, as we know, Haag had avoided these places, so he failed to secure any trace of the fugitive. Lacking his usual acumen, he did not stop at Jack Weber's tavern (Butcher Jack), and so missed the one opportunity of a trace of Haag.

Leaving the Elora Line at Alma, he travelled westwards to Creek Bank and the point of Woolwich Township. Thence going south he reached Elmira by nightfall, and put up at a tavern in that village for the night. Next morning he was early in the saddle, and travelling south for three miles, struck westwards about the same distance until he reached the Conestogo River. Following this up he finally reached Hawksville, and,

THE ARREST.

stabling his horse at a tavern, decided to remain a day or two in the locality.

On making inquiry of the tavern keeper, he found Peter Schneider was a substantial farmer living a mile north of the town. Exhibiting Haag's photo, he said he was looking for an acquaintance, but the tavern keeper declared he had never seen a man of that description in that neighbourhood.

Walking out to Schneider's after his dinner, he found the husband absent in Berlin, but Mrs. Schneider was at home and answered his knock. No, she had not seen her nephew Jack, nor her brother and wife since the fall before, when they had all been on a visit to her from the "Bush." What did he want with Jack? Oh, he was in the neighbourhood, knew Jack, and thought he would look him up.

After a pleasant chat on the weather, the folks up north in the "Bush," Laborde took his leave, convinced in his own mind that Jack Haag was not in Canada, but had cleared out to the Stars and Stripes and had joined Uncle Sam. The next point was to visit Saginaw and investigate that region.

Next morning he again mounted his horse, and travelling south through St. Clements and Heidelberg, reached Waterloo and Berlin by noon. Stabling his horse at the old Walper House he secured dinner, and advising the hotel man to look after his animal during his absence, which might be a week or more, went over to the Grand Trunk Station, where he took the first train westwards for Port Huron.

He reached Point Edward that night and crossed to Port Huron on the ferry. Here he found he would have to remain the whole day as there was only one train daily—about 5 p.m.—leaving Port Huron over the Père Marquette Railroad for Saginaw. He could have gone around by Durand and changed there on to a road running into Saginaw, but there would be little gain in time by so doing, so he decided to wait for the Père Marquette. He contented himself therefore by going to an hotel, engaging a room, and spending his time between reading the Chicago papers and sleeping.

At 5 p.m. he left for Saginaw over the Père

Marquette, and reached the lumber town about 10 o'clock that night. After breakfast the next morning, he inquired where Bridgeport lay, and finding it was about 3 miles south, secured a livery rig and drove out there. He found a small village of about 200 people surrounded by a thinly settled farming country.

Stopping at the only hotel in the place, he put up his horse and had his dinner. The landlord, a loquacious Yankee, endeavoured to " pump " the constable, but the latter was not a person to be " pumped." No, he was just a visitor in Saginaw, and had driven out to call on an acquaintance. Did the hotel man know anyone in that neighbourhood named Casper Haag? Oh, yes. He lived out south of the village about half a mile, and had rather a poor farm. Had he any family? No, only himself and wife—no children. Had he no nephew named Jack Haag with him? No, the hotel man had never heard tell of a nephew nor seen one. From time to time he had seen hired men on the farm, but no relations nor son.

Producing Jack Haag's photo, Laborde inquired :

" Did you ever see a man like that around here or at Haag's farm?"

" Oh, yes. A young fellow named John Miller came there about three weeks ago. That's the man," pointing to the picture, " but he's clean-shaven, while this picture shows a moustache," said the Boniface.

" He's probably shaved it off," remarked Laborde. " And you say his name is John Miller?"

"Yes. That's what he calls himself. Oh, he has been here many times on drinking bouts," replied the hotel man.

" Have you seen him lately?" asked Laborde.

" No, I haven't seen him for past three or four days.

I think he must be in Saginaw,'' replied the tavern keeper.

Laborde now deemed it wise to take the hotel man into his confidence, and after pledging him to secrecy told him that he was a constable from Canada, that the original of the photo was Jack Haag, wanted for murder in Bruce County, Upper Canada.

The hotel man at this opened his eyes and whistled.

"Well, he calls himself Miller around here. He is a drunkard, and I know he is a roué and gambler, because he has often boasted to me—in his cups—of his conquests,'' said the tavern keeper. "I'll bet you'll find him in Jim Barry's gambling joint in Saginaw.''

"I think I'll go out and interview Casper Haag on his farm,'' said Laborde. "Of course, you'll not give me away on this matter nor violate the confidence I've placed in you?''

"You bet I won't!'' replied the Boniface, whose name was Johnston. "I'll never shield a murderer, no matter who he is.''

Receiving explicit directions, Laborde then walked south from the village until he came to Casper Haag's home. It was a small frame dwelling, clap boarded, with its end facing the road, as so many American houses are built. On rapping on the door Casper Haag himself—a man in the 'sixties, gray-haired and gray-bearded—opened the door. His resemblance to his brother, old Gottlieb Haag, over in Upper Canada was marked.

"Good day! Is your man, John Miller, at home?'' inquired Laborde.

"No. Why do you want to see him?'' asked the gray-haired farmer, with a troubled look on his face.

"Oh, I come from Saginaw, and I've a little business

deal to transact with him," quickly replied the constable.

This seemed to relieve the old man, whose face cleared as he said :

" He has not been here for three or four days. I hired him for the summer to work on the farm, but I'll have to give him the sack if he goes on in this way. He is too much given to drink. I think he must be in Saginaw. Won't you come in and rest?" inquired the kindly old man.

" No. I must be getting back to town before dark. I'll probably see Jack Miller at another time," said Laborde. " Thank you, and good day."

" Good day !" replied the old man, the troubled look again returning to his face.

Laborde made haste in returning to Johnston's Hotel. On seeing the latter he acquainted him with the result of his visit. " I tell you what it is, Mr. Johnston," said Laborde. " Haag has made a clean breast of the murder to his uncle, and I know from the look on the old man's face when I asked for John Miller that he suspects who I am. Now, if I don't act quickly, he will notify the nephew and I will find my bird flown. Can you not come with me into Saginaw and show me to this Jim Barry's gambling den ? You will be well repaid for your trouble."

" Yes, I'll go with you. I'll never stand for murder," replied Johnston. " But see here ! First show me your warrant of arrest for this man !" cried the hotel man.

" Here it is," said Laborde, producing the paper with its formidable-looking red seal.

Johnston quickly perused it and said : " But you can't arrest him on this. This is only good in Canada.

Here you are in Michigan. You must go before a
magistrate here and swear to this, when a Michigan
warrant of arrest will be issued, and a Michigan constable will serve it when you come on your party,"
declared the hotel man.

"And in the meantime our man will get the alarm
and escape," said Laborde.

"It can't be helped," replied Johnston. "You must
have a proper warrant to arrest him on. He can't get
far away. I will go with you to a magistrate in
Saginaw. Come!"

Johnston hitched the horse to the buggy and the two
men quickly drove into Saginaw. Dusk was now falling, but Johnston knew the town well. Hastily
driving to a quiet street in the western part of the town,
they stopped before a large two-storey frame dwelling.
Hastily tying his horse to a hitching post, Johnston
knocked upon the door. A middle-aged lady opened
the door.

"Why, how do you do, Mr. Johnston!" she exclaimed. "Won't you come in?"

"Thank you, Mrs. Secord. Is Mr. Secord in?"
inquired the hotel man.

"No," replied the lady; "he left this morning for
Lansing—the State capital—and won't be home until
to-morrow night."

"How unfortunate!" exclaimed Johnston. "We
wished to see him on a very important matter. Is
there any other magistrate in this part of the town?"

"Yes. There's Mr. Morgan further down this
street at No. 144. He is pretty certain to be at home.
Is it anything very serious?" inquired Mrs. Secord.

"Yes. It's a matter of life and death, but I will tell
you about it to-morrow," said Johnston.

Thanking Mrs. Secord, the two men now hastily passed on down the street to No. 144 and found Judge Morgan at home. He was a man of 60 years of age, short and massive in build; a man of keen mind and few words. On telling him their errand he asked to see the warrant, which he read closely.

"You think your man is in Saginaw?" he asked, turning to Laborde.

"Yes, sir. Mr. Johnston here has identified him from this photograph," producing Jack Haag's photo from his pocket.

"Where is he to be found?" asked the Judge.

"I think he's most likely to be at Jim Barry's gambling and dance house," answered Johnston, "if his uncle, Casper Haag, hasn't already sent him the alarm to escape."

The Judge then had Laborde make oath as to the Canadian warrant, and then made out a Michigan warrant of arrest for the person of John Haag, alias John Miller, and directed them to take it to Henry Smith at No. 40, same street, who was a Michigan constable and empowered to serve Michigan warrants. On going to Smith's house they found him in bed, and grumblingly consented to "turn out" and take a "turn" at his duty.

During all this time Michael Laborde, Canadian constable, was on pins and needles as the different obstacles arose to render his efforts futile and allow of the escape of the murderer. Finally the three men tramped away to Barry's Dance Hall.

Jim Barry had been a lumber jack and river driver in his younger days, but now, a man of 50, he had settled down to a less precarious method of obtaining a living, and had opened a saloon dance hall and gambling joint

on West 10th Street. Here congregated the demi-
monde of the town. Here was the meeting place of
gamblers, roués, lumber jacks and all the riff-raff that
at that time frequented the lumber town of Saginaw.

In a large room 40 ft. long, crossed at its end by a
mahogany bar, on whose top a heavy brass rail of
shining brightness shone, and behind which three bar-
tenders supplied the needs of a thirsty throng, stood
Jim Barry. Behind him the wall was one huge mirror,
with decanters, glasses, silver and gilt which reflected
the light in a hundred scintillations, from the huge coal
oil lamp suspended from the ceiling and the many
lamps with reflectors attached to the walls.

Barry, as before mentioned, was a man of 50; blonde
and clean shaven; he had been a lumber jack and river
driver in his younger days; later he had taken to saloon
keeping in a small way, and now had been for two
years the keeper of the largest dance hall and gambling
joint in Saginaw.

At the upper end of the bar-room a door led into an
adjoining room or dance hall. Here, in a large room,
a dozen couples were whirling around in a dizzy waltz,
the wide hoop skirts of the ladies—which was the mode
of dress at that period—ballooning out in the circles of
the dance. On a raised platform at the end of the room
a man banged at a crazy piano, while a tall dark man
accompanied him on the violin.

Constable Smith, Johnston and Laborde entered the
saloon. The air of the room was heavy with tobacco
smoke, and crowded with river men, lumber jacks and
men of the town. Johnston plucked at Laborde's
sleeve and said:

"See there! Look at Barry! There is Casper
Haag speaking to him!" and he pointed through the
throng at Barry.

Laborde looked, and there, sure enough, was Casper Haag, the man he had interviewed that afternoon, in earnest conversation with the saloon keeper. The latter nodded his head, and making his way from behind the bar, opened the door leading into the dance hall and vanished.

"Officer!" cried Laborde to Constable Smith, "Barry is giving the alarm to the murderer. You must act quickly. Do not let him escape."

"All right! Come on! Follow me!" cried Constable Smith, and the three men, passing rapidly through the throng, opened the dance hall door and entered the adjoining room.

The waltz had now come to an end. The perspiring lumber jacks had led their "ladies" to seats around the walls and were standing idly conversing with them, while the latter waved fans to cool their heated faces. The musicians also were taking a merited rest. Looking rapidly around, Laborde saw Haag was not in the room, neither was Barry, but a door at the upper end of the room suggested an exit, and crying "Quick, Officer, or he will get away!" Laborde, followed by the two others, rushed across the room and threw open the door, disclosing a small room in which were apparently standing only two people—Jim Barry and an inmate of the dance hall called "Handsome Mag."

The latter stood in a corner of the room, her wide-hooped dress filling the space from wall to wall, while Barry stood beside a small table in the centre of the room. They had evidently been engaged in earnest conversation.

"What do you mean, you b——rs, by dashing into my house in this way?" cried Barry.

"I'm an officer of the law, Barry. Have a care what

you do!" cried Smith, the constable. "I have a warrant of arrest for John Haag, alias John Miller, for murder! Where is he?" cried Smith.

"I don't know where he is. He is not here," replied Barry. "Get out of my house! Your man is not here!" and Barry advanced upon the constable.

"See here, Barry!" exclaimed the constable, "you will get yourself into trouble by interfering with me in the performance of my duty."

"I don't care! Get out of my house!" shouted the saloon man, and he again advanced on the constable in a threatening manner.

During this altercation Laborde and Johnston had been silent witnesses of the scene. It now struck Laborde that the woman "Handsome Mag" was taking no part in the discussion and did not change her position in the corner.

"Will you come over here to the door, Miss? I wish to ask you a question," called Laborde.

"No, I won't!" replied "Mag." "I don't want any converse with you. Get out of the room!" and she crouched tighter against the wall.

Laborde walked over to her and, suddenly darting out his hand, grasped her by the arm and with a jerk dragged her away from the corner, disclosing Jack Haag in a crouching position on the floor.

Constable Smith jumped forward, and placing his hand on Haag's shoulder, cried out, "John Haag, alias John Miller, I arrest you in the name of the State of Michigan for murder! You are my prisoner!" and he slipped the handcuffs on Haag's wrists.

CHAPTER XXX.

THE TRIAL.

A Canadian Court of Justice is an awe-inspiring assemblage. The decorum, the slow but relentless pursuit of the truth during the proceedings, the black gown and clerical garb of the judge and prosecuting and defending counsel, the twelve intent jurymen listening to every word of evidence and upon whose verdict hangs the life of the accused man, the lone prisoner in his box facing judge and jury—all form part of a proceeding which forcibly impresses on the onlooker's mind the fact that here is being tried a matter of life and death.

Upon his arrest in Saginaw, John Haag had been thrown into jail in that town and three days thereafter was brought before an American judge on the charge of murder sworn by the Canadian constable. The bona fides of the Canadian warrant was looked into and the Canadian constable given extradition papers to remove Haag to Canada.

This had all been done and Haag had been brought to Walkerton and had since lain in the County gaol to stand trial for his life at the fall assize in that year.

Accordingly on Friday, September 18th, he was brought to trial before Judge Adam Wilson at Walkerton, the county town of Bruce. An immense crowd had gathered to hear the evidence. Bruce was stirred as never before. Here was the man who had disgraced them. The man who had committed a brutal and unnecessary crime upon a hard-working, law-abiding settler, schoolmate and neighbour! What a monster

he must be; and curiosity drew crowds to see what such
a man was like.   The court room was packed and
hundreds stood around outside unable to get an entrance
to the building.

At 10 o'clock the court crier called " Order," when
Judge Wilson in his black robes emerged from the
Judge's room, mounted the platform and sat down at his
desk.   The judge surveyed the crowded court room.
A pause followed and a side door opened and Michael
Laborde entered with the prisoner, Jack Haag, and
escorted him to the prisoner's box facing judge and jury.

How different now looked Haag from his appearance
in the previous winter—a pale, sallow face and sunken
black eyes, a shifty glance, betokened worry and sleepless nights.   The court crier read off the docket.   The
first case was—

The Queen versus Haag—Murder.

The jurymen then filed in and took their places in the
jury box, twelve good men and true, and had the oath
administered to them.   Their roll was called and each
answered to his name.   Their names were:

1. Thomas Black   2. William Sing
3. Robert Hall   4. Geddes Thompson
5. Robert McDonald   6. Charles Crow
7. Matthew Hammond   8. John Boyd
9. James Stark   10. Benjamin Lawton
11. Henry Dick   12. Joseph M. Gunn.

The first witness called was John Chambers, tavern
keeper, Belmore.   He mounted to the witness box and
took the oath.   Lawyer Gwynne (afterwards Justice
Gwynne), Counsel for the Crown, examined him.   Yes,
he kept tavern in Belmore and remembered the morning
of the 28th of the preceding February, and went on to
tell of the discovery of the inert and senseless form of
Stephen Neubecker, with a smashed face and head lying

in a sleigh in his driving shed at Belmore. How Neubecker had been tenderly carried into the hotel and cared for by his wife and maidservants, and that Dr. Kay of Walkerton was called to attend the stricken man and how he and Anthony Messner had followed the bloodstains to and from the scene of the murder, and of their visit to Grimm's and Miller's shanties on the same day, etc.

He was then asked to step down from the witness box, and Mrs. Chambers and her two maidservants— Hannah Day and Madeline Batty—were called. They testified to the condition of Neubecker when brought into the tavern, and what had been done for him.

Dr. Kay was then called and described the injuries the dead man had received, including the frost bites.

"Now Doctor," said the lawyer for the Crown, "I want to ask you a question and I want you to thoroughly consider it before answering, as I wish to be perfectly fair to the prisoner in the box. It is this—Had Neubecker not been exposed to the rigor of a winter's night, would he have recovered? In other words, was it the injuries to the head alone which killed Neubecker?"

After considering a moment Dr. Kay said, "Well, it's hard to say. Undoubtedly the injuries to the head caused him to lay outside all night exposed to the weather—so that the injuries caused the frost bite and both caused death."

"That's not answering my question!" cried the lawyer. "Would Neubecker have recovered had there been no frost bites? Yes or no?"

"He might have," replied the doctor, "it is possible; but the injuries caused him to receive the frost bites and because of both he died," replied the doctor.

"That will do, doctor. Please step down." George Grimm and Anthony Miller were now called and testified to the prisoner coming to their houses on the night of the murder, getting supper in one place and sleeping in the other.

Then Michael Laborde, the constable, and Anthony Messner gave their testimony as to what they had learned the day following the murder, and Laborde further described the steps he had taken both in Canada and Michigan to apprehend the murderer.

A number of other witnesses were then called to testify to minor points in the prosecution, Thomas Bennett, John and George Chambers, Sam Dickson, and Sam Price, John Fryfogle, Henry Toombs, Wm. Johnston, Peter Wickham and Chas. Haskin.

There was no defence! The jury then retired to consider their verdict, after being addressed by the judge as to the points of law brought out in the case. Court was then adjourned until 3 o'clock the same day and the prisoner returned to the gaol.

At 3 o'clock Court was re-convened and a message was sent from the jurymen that a verdict had been reached by the jury. The prisoner was again brought in from the adjoining gaol and placed in the prisoner's box. The court room was packed with people. A tense suspense filled all. The jury filed in and took their places. The Foreman, Robert Hall, arose and opening a paper faced the Judge and was asked by the Clerk :

" Have you reached a verdict?"

" Yes," replied the foreman. " Your Honour we unanimously find the prisoner John Haag guilty of murder !" and sat down. A thrill pierced the spectators and a low murmur of pity ran through the crowd.

" Order !" cried the court crier.

Haag visibly wilted on hearing the verdict. The Judge, addressing the jury, said—

"Gentlemen, I do not see from the evidence how you could have reached any other verdict!" Then putting on the Black Cap, while a tense stillness reigned in the room, he said:

"John Haag, stand up!" The prisoner attempted to do so but staggered and fell against the side of the prisoner's box and only with the constable's aid was he capable of assuming an upright position.

"John Haag," said the Judge. "you have had a fair trial by a jury of your peers and have been found guilty of the crime of murder. I will not add to the bitterness of to-day by commenting on what a cruel and brutal murder you have done, but only recommend that in the short time left to you on earth that you endeavour to obtain forgiveness for your crime from your Maker. My sentence is, that you be taken from hence to the place of confinement from which you came and be there kept until Tuesday the 15th day of December next, when at the hour of 10 o'clock of the forenoon of that day you be taken out and hanged by the neck until you are dead, and may the Lord have mercy on your soul!"

As the Judge concluded the prisoner collapsed in a dazed condition in the prisoner's box, and at the same time a low wail and a commotion at the doorway of the court room occurred, where old Gottlieb Haag, the aged father of the prisoner, had fallen to the floor in a faint.

The prisoner was then quickly taken into the adjoining gaol and the court room cleared. The poor old father was carried outside by friends, where he was revived and taken to his home.

And so ended Jack Haag's dream of long ago of a happy home and an honoured old age in the Queen's Bush! A Felon's death! His name a hissing and a by-word for all time to come by the men of Bruce!

CHAPTER XXXI.

A FATHER'S SUFFERING.

Old Gottlieb Haag was a man verging on 80 years of age. As a young man he had emigrated from Germany to America to seek his fortune and better his condition in the New World. Leaving Rotterdam in a sailing ship bound for New York, after a tedious and tempestuous voyage in which his ship was frequently blown half-way back to Europe, he finally landed on the shores of the New World. Here all his fortune lay before him. He realized that his success lay in himself and must come out of himself. Having secured a job as porter in a ship chandlery on Chambers Street, he remained at this work for five years when, tiring of city ways, brick walls and paved streets, he determined to go out into the country and get on to the land and till the soil as he had done in Germany years before.

Securing passage on one of the Hudson River boats, he landed one bright May morning at Albany and secured employment with a farmer neighbouring to the town.

Here he spent another five years of his life at service, but hearing of a large settlement of his countrymen at Berlin, Upper Canada, he determined he would set out for there.

Arriving at Buffalo he took train for Hamilton, and from thence by stage and wagon to Galt and thence to Berlin. Waterloo County at that time was being largely settled by emigrants from Pennsylvania—the Pennsylvania Dutch, they were called. Haag took up a small farm in Woolwich Township and worked it for several years, marrying in the meantime the daughter of a neighbouring settler. As his farm was small and the soil not of the best, when John Beaumont, his neighbour, decided to go to the Saugeen country where more land could be gotten for the taking, Haag also got the fever and followed him a few months later.

They now had a comfortable home in Western Brant; a good-sized clearing; solid log buildings and a good soil capable of growing anything that the hand of man could sow in that climate. Their one sorrow was their only son Jack; Jack as a child had been self-willed and headstrong, and because he was an only child had been petted and given his own way until he was spoiled, instead of being corrected and punished. As he grew to manhood he developed many vicious traits. First came liquor, for which he seemed to have an inordinate fondness, and following this he developed a desire for gambling. Though possessed of many good qualities—generous and forgiving in many things—these were more than overshadowed by his thirst for drink and his liking for low company, gambling, blaspheming and the pursuit of an idle and vicious life.

It seemed for a time, after coming to the " Bush " when his pursuit of Alice Beaumont appeared to him to augur favourably to his hopes, that he endeavoured to restrain himself and change his ways, but it did not last long. It is possible that had Alice Beaumont looked with favour on his suit, she might have controlled and reformed him and that his life would have been different. But Miss Alice quickly made it apparent to the densest mind that her choice did not lay with him. Haag pressed his suit the more ardently at this rebuff, but all in vain, and Hate being akin to Love, he shortly came to dislike as much as he had formerly loved the woman whom he had followed from Waterloo into the Queen's Bush, and never allowed to pass an opportunity to belittle or slander her. Such is Love and unrequited Love!

The year previous to Neubecker's murder, Jack Haag had seen little of his home. For a few days he would help the old father on the farm and then disappear for days together—off to Walkerton or to Orchard's Settlement at the mouth of the Mud River, or to the mouth at Southampton or Penetangore on the Lake.

There he was a constant inmate of the taverns; consorting and drinking and at times gambling with all the rough characters of the new settlements. His life was vicious, wicked, abandoned, and now to this viciousness had been added crime!

The days following the trial at Walkerton had been days of sorrow, heartaches and regrets for poor old Gottlieb and his aged wife.

"Oh! Father! Father! If he would only die before he is hanged! The awful horror and disgrace of being hanged before all the people! Father it will kill me!" exclaimed the poor old mother.

"My boy! My boy!" she sobbed, "Oh why did you do it?" and the aged woman cast herself upon a couch and sobbed as if her heart would break.

Old Gottlieb sat down by his wife's side and taking the old gray head in his lap, said, "Never mind, mother. Do not worry. Perhaps a way will be found," and he stroked the gray hair of the poor mother and he kissed her and fondled her as in the days of their courtship.

This picture of an old gray-headed couple—alone with their sorrow—no hand stretched out to help—no kindly voice to assuage the bitterness of their life—mourning for a wayward son, was one capable of turning a heart of stone to pity.

On the morrow Gottlieb Haag, kissing his wife good-bye, wended his way to Walkerton, the county town, and passing down the Main Street entered at the farther end a small frame dwelling, upon whose window a sign "Dr. M., Physician and Surgeon," was painted, and acquainted the public that a member of the healing art dwelt there. Opening the door he entered a small room which served as the Doctor's office—a couple of chairs, a table, a couch, a washstand and basin and behind it on the wall a few shelves, on which were an array of bottles with medicine, formed the furniture of the room. The noise of Haag's entry caused the opening of a door into the rear of the office, through which entered Dr. M. himself.

Dr. M. was a tall man, in the prime of life; his face was adorned with a heavy black beard and he had piercing black eyes and spoke with a marked Scotch accent. "Hech! it's Master Haag! And hoo are you Master Haag? I'm pleased to see you and at the same time you have my sympathy for you and yer guid wife in yer trouble!" and the Doctor shook the old man warmly by the hand.

"That's the very thing I've come to see you about, Doctor," said old Gottlieb.

"What? Hoo?" exclaimed the doctor.

"About Jack," answered the old man. "If he's publicly hanged the disgrace and horror of it will kill his mother! Can you not give me something that can be slipped to him and so avoid the gallows?"

"So! And that's your errand here, man? Yer wanting me to commit murder, too, by giving ye poison for yer son? Na! na! man! None o' that!" and the Doctor vigorously shook his head. "Waes me!

waes me! what a world! I wouldna thocht it o' ye, Gottlieb Haag, to add the crime o' poisoning to that o' murder in yer family!" and again the Doctor vigorously shook his head.

" Oh, Doctor! consider! He is our only boy. He was our hope. And now! His mother and I have suffered the bitterness of death since the trial. Can you not help us?" and with tears streaming down his cheeks the old gray-haired man held out his hands in mute appeal and turned a supplicating face upon the medical man.

The Doctor was evidently strongly moved and gazed at the floor in thought. At length he raised his head and said, " Weel! I'll see what I can do. But it 'ill no be in the way you think. I'll journey to Toronto to-morrow and see about it. But don't build on it. Come tae me in a week's time but keep a still tongue in yer heid aboot the matter," and shaking hands with the aged farmer he saw him to the door and bidding him good-bye returned to his office.

Old Gottlieb returned home, his spirits elated by what the Doctor had said. Evidently, he thought, the Doctor would see the Governor of Upper Canada and obtain a pardon for Jack, or at least a term of imprisonment and Jack's life would be spared!

The old man returned to the farm imparting to his aged wife the joyful news that Dr. M. had interested himself in the case and would see what could be done to save Jack's life. There was no doubt that Neubecker had died from exposure and he might secure a pardon or at least a sentence of life imprisonment. With such thoughts as these do the aged nourish hope and grasp at straws.

At the expiration of a week's time old Gottlieb made another pilgrimage to the county town for another

interview with Dr. M. He was kindly received as
before by the medical man, who after some general
observations on the weather and the results of the
harvest, said—

" I was in Toronto and partly arranged the matter,
but there's yet another man to see. I dunno but it may
cost you too much siller, Master Haag, to carry oot.
The Toronto party wants $500 for his services. What
the other yane'll want I'll no say."

" No matter what it will cost Doctor. Take my little
farm if it will save his life! Oh! Anything! Anything! If it will save his life and give him a chance to
repent!" and the old man trembled in his eagerness.

" Ye must onderstand Master Haag, that onything
I'm doing is no for money. I'm doing it for you and
yer puir auld wife, whom I peety from my heart; and
another thing ye must swear tae me on the Holy Bible
ye'll no utter a word o' what I'm going tae tell ye about
the matter, not even tae yer guid wife. Ye must be as
sacret as death," solemnly replied the Doctor, as arising
he went into an inner room and shortly returned with a
large Bible in his arms.

" Noo! Stan' up, Gottlieb Haag. Take this Holy
Buik in yer hands, open and kiss it and solemnly swear,
in the presence of yer Maker, never to divulge what ye
hear in this room to-night."

Old Gottlieb quickly arose, and taking the Holy Book
in his hand opened and kissed it, and then holding up
his right hand to Heaven solemnly swore never to dis-
close whatever information the Doctor might impart to
him that night.

Sitting down again the Doctor drew his chair close to
that of Gottlieb and held him in earnest conversation for
the next half hour. A variety of expressions chased
across the old man's face as he listened to the Doctor's

tale—at first unbelief was pictured there—then interest and hope and finally joy was written on his features as he exclaimed—

"And you think it will succeed, Doctor?"

"Perfectly certain! I hae seen it done! And in another land than this. Far, far frae here. Far away in my hame i' the north! Ah me! Ah me! Why did I ever leave my hame in yon bonnie lan' to come tae this wild contree?" and the Doctor fell into a brown study.

"Oh! Doctor you are my friend for life. I am an old man and my span of life cannot last much longer but you have taken the bitterness out of the short time I have to live. If you succeed I shall go to my grave with contentment!" and the aged farmer wrung the Doctor's hand in an ecstasy of thankfulness.

"Noo! Not a word mair! Come in when you happen to be in toon and I will tell ye hoo the matter goes on! But!" placing his finger on his lips, "mum's the word!"

Old Gottlieb arose, gratitude in his face, and after warmly shaking the doctor's hand, departed.

The following evening after the conversation Dr. M. put on his cap and overcoat and taking a back street, made his way rapidly to the County gaol. Rapping on the door of the Turnkey's quarters—which formed part of the gaol premises—Mrs. Meyer, wife of the gaol turnkey, opened the door.

"Is George aboot, Mistress Meyer? I want to see him for a few minutes!" the Doctor asked.

" He is just going to bed!" replied the woman.

" Well tell him I only want to see him for a moment!" cried the doctor.

A few minutes thereafter George entered the room and greeted the medical man.

" Good night, doctor ! You are late on your rounds !"

" How do you do, George ! I only kem in to ask you to step doon to my office to-morrow evening after you hae locked up the prisoners for the nicht. I hae a little business I wish to discuss wi you !" said the doctor.

To this George readily consented and after a few general observations the doctor took his leave.

The following evening, Meyer called at the doctor's office. The latter after shaking hands with him, placed a chair and locking the office door so they would not be interrupted sat down and engaged the Turnkey in earnest conversation for some time. As the talk proceeded Meyer began shaking his head exclaiming " It would be too dangerous and if discovered I would lose my job and perhaps land in gaol myself !"

" Na ! Na ! Not a bit of it. It wull succeed and ye'll no risk yer job, I tell ye—besides ye'll be well paid fer it ! I am deputed to offer ye $300 for yer help ! Wull ye take it ?"

This large sum of money—for at that period it was a large sum—seemed to excite the cupidity of the turnkey, for he asked—

" When will the money be paid ?"

" It'll be paid ye the nicht before the hanging !" answered the doctor.

After some further consideration, Meyer nodded his consent to the arrangement, concluded the bargain and departed.

The time now drew on to the date of Haag's hanging. October, with its rain and muddy highways, came and went. November, with its frosts and snows also passed away, and now came the first week in December and the execution was only a week away.

One day Dr. M. met Sheriff Sutton on the street and accosted him thus :—

"Weel Shurra, hoo are ye! Ye'll be having a nice necktie party up tae yer jail, next week! Hae ye gotten a man tae tie the necktie for ye!" cried the doctor as he looked with a leer into Sheriff Sutton's face.

Sheriff Sutton was a very humane man and was no believer in capital punishment. "What the Lord gave the Lord should take away!" was his belief, nevertheless, by virtue of his office he was obliged—no matter how much it went against his own feelings—to carry out the law and see that Haag was hanged.

"Oh! Doctor! Doctor!" he replied, "what a callous slaughterhouse lot of men you doctors are! You have no more regard for a man's neck than you have for a chicken's. Fie man! Haag is a human being, with feelings like your own, and his life to him is as dear as yours is to you!" and the Sheriff shook his finger at the Sawbones.

"Weel! Na doot ye are richt, Shurra! It was just a manner o' speaking. But hae ye gotten a hangman for the job yet?" and the Doctor looked at the Sheriff sharply.

"Oh! Yes! I was in Toronto last week and was advised to see a certain party by the Attorney General. His name is Dan Beasley. He is a rake and gambler and is usually found at Fred Diamond's Nippissing Hotel on King St. East. He has already done similar jobs, but the villain is very dear! He is charging me $100 for the job and you know it must be paid out of my salary and which you also know is very small!" answered the sheriff with indignation.

"Hoots mon! That's naething! If it's too much, why cashier Beasley and do the job yerself and so save $100!" and the doctor burst into a huge guffaw at the nonplussed sheriff, and turned away, laughing, as he made his way down the street.

CHAPTER XXXII.

THE BARGAIN.

At the period of which we write—the opening of the Queen's Bush—the old Nippissing Hotel stood on the corner of King and George Streets, Toronto. It was a notable resort in the old days. Though mainly patronized by the farmers from the neighbouring townships and the citizens living in the eastern end of the city.

Late hours, bibulous parties and card games were frequent within its doors. Its proprietor was Fred Diamond, a fair-complexioned man, short and stubby in stature and of about 40 years of age. He was a dandy in dress, in fact a "dude." He had made a little money —enough to give him a start as an hotel keeper, in a rented building. He kept a good table, for his main clients—the farmers—would only patronize a stopping place where the food was of the best.

At that time, a rivalry had sprung up amongst these farmer hotels in the eastern end of the city—" The Black Horse " on Front Street; " The Clyde " on King St.; " The Nippissing " also on King, and " John Wright's Hotel " on Queen Street. All vied in giving the best meals for the price—25c.—to their most numerous clientele, the farmers. The groaning tables were supplied with all the good things of life. Hotel meals in the early fifties were not as those of to-day. Food was not doled out in tablespoonful doses—each dose in a small dish of its own and surrounding the diner's plate. Not at all! A roast of beef occupied one end of a long table, a roast of pork the other, while in between these positions and in profusion were dishes of cabbage, onions, potatoes, carrots, radishes, parsnips, turnips, pies, puddings, cakes, preserves, bread and butter. From these dishes the diner helped himself.

Diamond had seen hard times in his youth and had learned, in a hard school, the value of a dollar. He was therefore out to make money, by respectable means if possible, but to make money. His house was the resort of many shady characters, who as long as they spent their money freely were welcomed by Diamond.

Although the License law at that time enjoined the closing of the bar at 10 o'clock—still card parties gathered in other rooms and secured all the liquor they wanted and carried on games, betting and drinking far into the night.

Amongst the hotel's many frequenters was one Dan Beasley, a rake and gambler. This man had been left a prosperous business of tinsmithing on Queen St. East by his father, but after the latter's death, Dan rapidly went to the dogs with drink, gambling and neglect of business.

He was a man of 40 years of age, inclined to corpulency, with cold blue eyes, bloodshot from booze, of a determined nature, vindictive, cool and calculating.

His pal and chum was Ed Smith, another roué and gambler and boozer. These with a few kindred spirits, Abe Law, Jack O'Fallard (Cowboy Jack), Tom Ochiltree and Fred Lawson made up a coterie whose nights were spent in Diamond's rooms, drinking and gambling.

On the present occasion—an evening in the late fall, they were engaged in a game of euchre at a dollar a side. Dan and Ed. being opposed to Abe and Tom Ochiltree. Abe Law was dealing and turned up "Hearts."

Hearts were Trumps! Beasley cried out " I order it up and play it alone!"

" Be careful Dan!" cried his partner Ed. " The b --- r may fleece you!"

" Fleece nothing!" exclaimed Dan. " There's never a Law nor Ochiltree whom I can't fleece now or any day!" throwing down on the table with a slam the Ace of Hearts. This brought out the Queen from Tom and the ten spot from Abe. Dan raked them in and led again with the Jack of Hearts which brought out Spades and Clubs from Abe and Tom. After raking these in, Dan with a triumphant leer again led a trump, the King which drew out the remaining black cards in the hands of his opponents, thereby winning the game and money for Dan.

" Aw! H--l this is child's play. Give me Poker! At $5 a chip! This is d--n dry work, Diamond! Bring us up hot whisky!" cried out Beasley.

Ochiltree and Law took up the challenge. A poker deck was brought. Chips sold, and the game began.

The players were the same as in the euchre game— Dan and Ed and Abe and Tom Ochiltree.

Ed. Smith opened the game and Dan Beasley raised him. Abe Law quit cold. Tom Ochiltree then looked around with a funny smile and tilted the pot the limit. Dan Beasley came right back at him—playing reckless as it were and that let Dan out. All his money was on the table.

" All through?" says Tom Ochiltree, looking at Beasley out of one eye.

" All through is right!" says Dan.

" Well!" says Tom, " you may have something but I doubt it. I hope you haven't gone and bet foolishly being so green at the game!" and Tom grinned aggravatingly in Beasley's face.

" What have you got ? "

Dan laid down the three Kings and says :

" The pot's mine ! "

Tom said " That's a right smart hand you got Mr. Dan Beasley, but I guess I got you beat ! " and with that he laid down a full house.

" Just missed it ! " says Tom reaching for the pot. Beasley uttered a curse and called for Diamond to bring more liquor. Presently Diamond entered with a steaming jug of hot water in one hand and a decanter of whisky in the other.

" There's a party below looking for you, Dan ! " said the hotel man.

" Who is it ? " asked Beasley.

" I don't know his name ! " returned Diamond. " He is tall, black-bearded, and speaks with a strong Scotch accent. Better go down and see what he wants ! "

After drinking a steaming glass of hot whisky, Beasley arose and making his way downstairs, entered the sitting room of the Hotel—adjoining the bar—and found his visitor to be our old acquaintance Dr. M. of Walkerton.

" Good evening sir ! " said M. " I understand you are Dan Beasley ? "

" That is my name ! " said Beasley. " What is it you want with me ? " and he looked enquiringly at his visitor.

" Weel ! My name is M.; I'm a doctor frae Walkerton in Bruce County and I am also surgeon to the gaol there. I understand Sheriff Sutton of Bruce has engaged you to act as hangman at the coming execution of John Haag, for murder, on December 15th next, at Walkerton ! " replied the Doctor.

" Yes ! I've made an arrangement with the Sheriff to do the job for him. But he's a very tight-fisted sheriff. He's not giving me near what the job is worth. However, what have you to do with the matter? What is it you want with me?" observed Beasley.

"Weel! It's this!" and the doctor entered upon an earnest conversation with the hangman which lasted for half an hour or more. Finally Beasley exclaimed. "Well! It's $500 or nothing. If I succeed it will be cheap at the price!"

"Weel! It may be! I'll no say it's not! But who would want sich a life as Haag must lead at your or any price, is mair nor I can tell!" and the doctor shook his head vigorously. "And the measures you speak of and the appliances—where are they to be gotten?" asked Beasley. "Oh! They'll be furnished tae ye, my man —the measurements and directions. I'll attend to that myself as soon as I return home!" replied the doctor.

After some further discussion of the matter, Dr. M. bade Beasley good-night and left the Hotel, while Beasley after pondering the matter in hand for a short time slowly mounted the stairs to the gambling room above.

CHAPTER XXXIII.

THE HANGING.

DECEMBER 15th was the day set for the hanging of
Jack Haag. As the fatal day approached, hurried
preparations were made by the conspirators to carry out
their allotted parts. Sheriff Sutton's known repugnance
to hanging was apprehended, appreciated and taken advantage of. Beasley had had the apparatus for Jack
Haag's neck and shoulders made in Toronto (from
written directions sent him by Dr. M.), the measurements for which had been taken by one of the other conspirators—Dr. M.—in his position as gaol surgeon at
Walkerton. This of course had to be done surreptitiously, but as the turnkey was another paid member of
the conspiracy, no hint at the proposed attempt to frus-
trate the ends of justice had leaked out to the authorities,
nor of course to the outside world.

The apparatus consisted of a sort of flat steel shoulder-
brace—in which two steel curved arms, well padded,
passed under each armpit, curving from behind forwards. These were united behind to a two-inch broad
band of steel, which ran up the back, between the
shoulder blades and projected half way up the neck in
a flat band of steel, where it turned downwards, forming
a short curve. This apparatus was to be worn below
the shirt and next the skin.

The apparatus was not noticeable, being covered by
the clothing. The portion above the collar was, it is
true, visible, but if Haag wore his hair long—and no
doubt due to this he had refused to have his hair cut

during his incarceration in the County Gaol—covered by the hair the steel band and hook could not be seen.

A few days before the hanging Dr. M. had made a hurried trip by stage to Guelph over the Elora Road—thence by rail to Toronto, and had carefully inspected the apparatus at Dan Beasley's shop.

"I don't see how the d---l you're going to save Haag's neck with that contraption!" said Dan Beasley.

"Vera easy, sair!" said the doctor, "Vera easy! Ye ken maist criminals that are executed by hanging are choked to death. But if the recht drop for the wecht o' the body is calculated, the heid with the atlas—which ye ken is the first bone o' the spinal column, is torn frae the axis—which ye ken is the second bone o' the same spinal column and which has a projection extending upwards frae its body. When these bones are disrupted, this projection pierces the medulla, which ye ken is the lower pairt o' the brain, and the man dies instantly. If the wecht o' the body is too great or the drop too far, the heid may be torn frae the body, while if either is too short, the man is simply choked to death and that may take 20 minutes or half an hour!"

"With this appliance the jerk o' the rope is carried to the armpits, and the neckbones are no disrupted and its your pairt to see he is no choked to death!"

"How in h---l can I do that?" exclaimed Beasley.

"Just by placing a knot in the loop of your rope, that the loop will tighten so far and no farther and the man is suspended by his armpits!" answered the doctor.

"Will the steel hook at the back of his neck not be seen?" asked Beasley.

"Nay! nay! The steel hook is flat and projects just aboot half way up his neck. It will be maistly covered by his shirt and long hair whilst your black cap will cover it where the hook engages the rope!" returned the doctor. " Na! Na! Man! Dinna fear! Never fash yer heid aboot it sir! It will save his neck! I willna say, if ye leave him hanging too long but perhaps he micht die—at ony rate be insensible; but he'll no die very quickly wi yon against his thrapple!"

" Well! We'll see! But I'm doubtful," exclaimed Beasley. " I will do my best!"

" Ye ken man!" continued M. " Every hangman should be an anatomist and know very intimately the pairts o' the human body that he has to deal wi' in his trade! He should also be an artist and be capable to ' turn off ' the culprit expeditiously and wi' due decorum and no struggling and straining o' arms or laigs that the onlookers may no be upset by their feelin's and hae to puke or maybe run off holding their hand to their mooths! Man! man! I hae seen some terrible botches at they hangings, years lang syne!" and the doctor helped himself to two huge pinches of snuff from his snuff box. " Man! the law never intended cruelty in executing its punishments. 'Twas always the bungling o' the hangman which caused a horror. He gave too much rope or too little."

December 15th came, bright and clear. The ground was frozen hard, and a light fall of snow the night before had covered the ground. From early morn, crowds of people had been wending their way towards the county town. The hour for the hanging had been set for 10 o'clock. Long before that hour a huge crowd of people had gathered before the eastern wall of the gaol, where the hanging was to take place.

The county gaol and court house was surrounded by a high stone wall—probably 15 feet high. Inside this wall and on its eastern side and within the gaol grounds, a scaffold had been erected, with a stairway leading up to its platform—which was on a level with the top of the wall; and with its lower frame-work boarded up in order that none of the gaol inmates could see the struggles of the dying man after the drop.

Many of the crowd of onlookers had come long distances that morning to witness the execution. In those days, quite different from the present—hangings were a public event or spectacle and were so held as a warning to evil-doers. In fact in some of the surrounding country schools, the teachers had declared a holiday and had exhorted their pupils to attend and witness the execution and to take it as a warning never to commit a crime! Such then was the setting!

Shortly before 10 o'clock a procession formed in the gaoler's office. First came the Sheriff, Wm. Sutton, holding his Warrant of Execution. By his side was the Rev. Mr. I----, a Church of England clergyman, following whom was Dr. M., the gaol physician, Beasley the hangman, and, bringing up the rear, the turnkey George Meyer.

The procession passed down the gaol corridor to the cell of the condemned man. Turnkey Myer unlocked and threw open the cell door and discovered Haag on his knees at prayer. This gave the procession pause, when Haag arose and said:

" Mr. Sheriff, I am ready!"

Sheriff Sutton opened out his warrant and said—

" John Haag, you have had a fair trial by a jury of your peers and have been adjudged guilty of murder. My warrant reads: ' To Wm. Sutton, Sheriff of the County of Bruce, you are to take the body of John Haag, condemned murderer, and confine it in the County Gaol, at Walkerton, until December 15th next, when at the hour of 10 o'clock in the forenoon of that day, you are to take the said body of John Haag and hang it by the neck until dead and may God have mercy on his soul.

Signed Adam Wilson, J.U.C.' "

Hangman Beasley then advanced and pinioned Haag's arms behind his back by means of straps. The procession then re-formed, with Beasley and the condemned man leading—the others following—down the corridor and out into the gaol yard. The steps to the scaffold were then mounted and the condemned man placed on the drop—a hinged door in the flooring, while the clergyman, Sheriff Sutton and Dr. M., ranged in a

THE HANGING.

semi-circle on the platform. The noose of the rope dangled from the cross-beam overhead.

" You are at liberty to say a few words to the people, Haag, if you so wish !" said the Sheriff in a low voice.

John Haag gazed around at the assembled multitude and tears came to his eyes as he recognized many faces of his old acquaintances amongst the throng.   With an effort he overcame his emotion and said :

"Men !   I am about to die !   I acknowledge I am receiving just punishment for what I have done !   In my right senses I would never have committed the act for which I am about to suffer, but liquor and fast living have brought me to this.   I wish to warn all young men against the three influences which have ruined my life.

'Wine, women and song
      Keeps a man poor his life long.'

"I have asked God's forgiveness for my crime and forgive all my enemies !" Turning to Beasley the hang-man he said "I am ready !"

Haag's knees and ankles were then quickly strapped together and the noosed rope adjusted to the neck ; the black cap drawn over the head and face and Beasley stepped off the trap.

The Rev. Mr. I ---- began the Lord's Prayer, at the words "Forgive us our trespasses," Beasley pulled the lever releasing the drop and Haag's body shot down-wards out of sight !

As Haag's body disappeared, Sheriff Sutton turned white and sank to the floor in a faint.   The Rev. Mr. I ---- rushed to his support and raised him up and as he came to, supported him down the scaffold and to his rooms in the gaol, whilst Beasley and Dr. M. descended to the enclosure below the scaffold, where the other con-spirator—the turnkey George Meyer—had already gone. The body of Haag was still suspended and the rope swaying gently to and fro.   M. advanced and placing his finger on the pulse nodded his head and then pulling off the black cap from the face pulled up an eyelid.

"The lad's a' richt !   He's just having a wi bit sleep and is only a wi' bit blue i' the face.   Lift him up Meyer, and Beasley loosen the rope frae the neck !"   This was done and Haag was laid out upon the ground, where his arms and legs being released from the straps, he was placed upon his back. Dr. M. then crouching astride the body seized the arms of the hanged man, and began to move them slowly backwards and forwards in artificial respiration.

Faintly at first but increasing in depth as the doctor continued his labours—the respirations increased and shortly Haag gave a gasp and opened his eyes and staring around him hoarsely whispered " Where am I ?"

" Yer no in Heaven, me lad, and ye micht hae been in t'other place had we no worked upon ye. Wae's me ! Wae's me ! What a world !" exclaimed the doctor.

THE APPARATUS THAT SAVED HAAG'S NECK.

M's apparatus had done its work. The only mark on the culprit's neck was at the front where the rope had left a bluish welt—for the rest the flat steel hook behind had saved him.

" Noo ! My lad ! We're going to save ye but ye must ein help yerself ! We'll put ye in this coffin— where provision is made ye'll no stifle, and ye must lie there till nicht, when we'll bury the coffin, but before the coffin is committed to the earth, ye'll hae yer resurrection ! Noo ! I warn ye keep still till nicht !"

During this harangue, Haag had frequently put his hand to his neck, under the chin where the rope had chafed him.

He was lifted up and placed in the coffin, whose ends were perforated and cunningly concealed for air. The lid was screwed down and the coffin left in the enclosure. The three conspirators then re-entered the gaol where Beasley and Meyer went to the turnkey's kitchen for refreshment, while the doctor went on to the gaoler's quarters to see how Mr. Sutton did. He found the latter reclining on a couch with the clergyman sitting by his side. "Hoo are ye feeling the noo, Master Sutton?" inquired the doctor.

"I am better! But oh it was an awful sight to see the man plunge to his death, with that rope around his neck! I will see it in my dreams for months to come!" declared the sheriff.

"Tut! Tut! Ye'll soon forget it, man! And he made a pretty job of it, yon Beasley! Indeed he did!" and the doctor rubbed his hands briskly. "Haag is lying out there in his coffin and it will be buried the nicht! Burying a murderer is no a job to be done in broad daylight!" declared the doctor.

"Will you bury the body in the gaol yard?" the sheriff asked weakly.

"Na. His father asked that his son be buried outside the toon where they could at times visit his grave, which they could no do if he were buried in the gaol premises!" replied the doctor.

"Well! Well! Have it so! It matters little where the poor fellow is buried!" declared the sheriff and turned his face to the wall. Presently M. left the room.

"What a brutal fellow that doctor is! He thinks no more of hanging a man than of killing a chicken!" exclaimed the sheriff. "Yes!" replied the clergyman, "their trade makes them callous!"

That night at 10 o'clock a one-horse wagon driven by Beasley arrived at the gaol gate. The turnkey opened the latter and the conveyance was driven to the scaffold. The coffin was brought out by the turnkey Meyer and Beasley and lifted on to the conveyance. Dr. M. had in the meantime come out and taken his seat on the wagon along with the turnkey, who acted as driver, while Beasley the hangman seated himself upon the coffin. The wagon then drove away to the grave which had been dug on a vacant lot just outside the southwest part of the town and close beside a small vacant barn.

Here the wagon stopped, the coffin was lifted off and conveyed into the ramshackle structure, where Beasley unscrewed the lid and helped Haag to a sitting posture and out of his receptacle; the latter was then filled with stones and conveyed by the three men outside to the open grave where it was lowered by ropes to the bottom.

Beasley and Meyer then hastily shovelled in the earth until the grave was filled—the doctor holding the lantern to guide them at their work.

Presently the earth was heaped into a mound and patted down, with sloping sides, and the task was finished.

The men then returned to the shed where Haag had been left sitting in moody silence.

"Noo! My lad!" said the Doctor, "we're finished wi ye and ye must een shift for yersel! I wad advise ye to remain here for a couple o' hoors and after midnight haste away to yer farther's hoose, where ye micht lie concealed for a few days to recover yer strength and then haste away to another land than this, where I hope ye may live a better life, for if ye remain in this country ye'll be caught and the next time ye'll hang for good!"

Good-byes were uttered and the party returned to the town, leaving Haag alone in the barn!

CHAPTER XXXIV.

THE AFTERMATH.

THE little town of B----- in Shiawasse County, Michigan, nestles in the valley of the Shiawasse River. This valley ran north and south with high hills on either bank, enclosing a valley of perhaps half a mile in width. Back of the hills, to the east and to the west, were rolling farming lands, interspersed with scattered clumps of timber—pine and walnut and elm.

The town of B----- was built on each side of the river, with its Main Street at right angles to the stream and spanning the latter by a bridge. It was a farmer's town with businesses suitable for trade with a farming community—a grist mill, stores—general and hardware and furniture, post office and telegraph office, tailor, butcher and machine repair shops, an undertaker's shop, a foundry, tannery, brewery and woollen mill, and what not.

Ten years after the events recorded in the preceding chapter, at the close of an autumn day, a man verging on to middle life, but with graying hair, emerged from one of the shops on the Main Street and began putting up the window shutters of the store. Re-entering the building, he threw off his apron, put on his coat, closed and locked the door and took his departure. He slowly wended his way westwards to the outskirts of the town, to where stood a pretty blue and white cottage, surrounded by a hawthorn hedge and catalpa tree.

As he approached the house, the voices of children were heard and as he closed the garden gate its noise brought a little curly-headed lad of 5 years, with blue eyes and fair hair, rushing out with a whoop, crying :

"Oh! Daddy! Daddy! Mamma has pancakes and maple syrup for supper! Aren't you glad?"

"Yes Davie! Pancakes are my favourite dish!" said the father and lifting up the little lad to a sitting position on his shoulder he carried him into the house, the arms of the youngster encircling his father's neck.

At the door he was met by his wife.

"You are very late, John! I've had supper ready the last half hour!"

"Yes! I know Mary, but I was very busy and couldn't get off sooner!"

"Well! Come on! Supper is on the table!" said his wife.

The family consisted of the man, his wife Mary, and two children—Davie whom we have seen, a boy of 5 years of age, and the baby named Katie, a dark-eyed, dark-haired little witch of 3 years. As they sat down to the supper table his wife remarked "The new Minister, the Rev. Mr. Smith, called this afternoon and introduced himself. He said he would call again some evening in order to meet you!"

"What is he like?" asked the husband. "Oh! He is a young man with blue eyes and brown hair and short whiskers and very enthusiastic in his work!"

"I do not take much stock in those preachers, Mary! Many of them do not practise what they preach! They preach the Golden Rule but they do not practise it! ' Do as I tell you, not as I do!' is their motto!"

"Why John Miller! How ever can you say such a thing!" exclaimed his wife. "They are the poorest and most deserving class in a community! The idea!"

"Well! Now Mary, I will give you only one instance, out of many, that I've seen in my life time.

Back home, when I was a boy, our Minister was the Rev. Mr. B-----h. He was a very grasping man after money. He had a large congregation at his home church and a good salary. Besides this he had two other congregations to attend to in the same township, composed of wealthy farmers.

" My father was a poor farmer who worked hard on his little farm of 50 acres to support his family and make ends meet. One winter, after a poor harvest, when fodder was scarce and dear and my father was hard put and in straits to make up his taxes, the Rev. Mr. B-----h called on him and asked him for a load of hay and straw, from my father's little store— for his horse and cows— for the Minister kept two or three of the latter, pasturing them on the highway, and sold the cream and the butter.

" My father, thinking he would get a little ready money to pay his own debts, took him a small load of each commodity and expected, as the Rev. B-----h was a well-paid Minister of the Church, to receive at least a little cash for his fodder. But nothing was said as to payment.

Some ten days later the Rev. B-----h and his wife drove up to my father's house to spend the evening—a ministerial call upon a parishioner. My poor mother gave them the best of her scanty larder for their refreshment. On rising to leave about 9 o'clock the Rev. Mr. B-----h advanced to my father, took him by the hand and said :

" ' Well ! Mr. M. I wish to thank you kindly for the gift of the hay and straw which you so kindly donated to the Church ! The Lord will reward you for your generosity to his servant,'—and with that he and his wife took their departure. My father could only stand

and stare with mouth and eyes open, endeavouring to see his vanishing dollars."

"Oh John Miller!" exclaimed his wife. "You are the limit! You know ministers are proverbially poor!"

"Well! This one I speak of, was not. He had a salary from three congregations, besides all the fees from christenings, marriages and burials! And he knew my father was poor and in straits! I tell you they are all tarred with the same brush!" said John vehemently. "Mammon is their God and they use their calling to feather their own nests!"

"Well I'm sure the Rev. Mr. Smith is not like that!" retorted his wife. "Though neat, his clothes were shining from long wear and his cuffs and trouser bottoms were frayed and he wore a celluloid collar, and you know a celluloid collar only requires the laundering a damp rag can give it and he spoke so enthusiastically of all the good he hoped to achieve amongst the poor children of the town!" said his wife.

"Well! We'll see!" said the husband and the meal proceeded.

The following evening the Rev. Mr. Smith called at the Miller house and was introduced by Mrs. Miller to her husband.

The Minister was a young man of about 30 years of age; of medium stature; with blue eyes, a short brown beard, moustache and brown hair. He was of an optimistic nature and very enthusiastic in his work.

"I am very pleased to meet you, Mr. Miller. I have heard much of the kindness of your heart and your work on behalf of our Church since my coming to H----," and the Minister shook hands warmly with John Miller.

"Yes!" said Mrs. Miller, "and he has only just finished giving me a lecture on the present-day

Mammon-loving preachers of the Gospel! Now what do you think of that?"

"Well! Perhaps his bark is worse than his bite!" replied the clergyman.

"Now Mary! You know that isn't fair! I was only speaking generally!" cried Miller, reddening under his wife's charge.

The evening passed pleasantly.

The Rev. Mr. Smith proved to be a good mixer. He was a good conversationalist, had travelled considerably over the universe; had come in contact with many classes of people in his different charges but withal was at heart a good man, who believed in his fellow men and offered help—whatever lay in his power to furnish—when help was needed.

After a pleasant evening he took his leave, first extending a warm invitation to John Miller to call and visit him of an evening. This Miller promised to do.

A few evenings after this visit, John Miller called at the clergyman's home. He found the latter ensconced in his library evidently at work upon the following Sunday's sermon. On seeing who his visitor was, the clergyman arose and warmly welcomed him to his house and led him to a cosy chair by a warm stove.

The room was small but comfortable. Two bookcases well filled with books occupied one side of the room; a large library table on which stood a shaded lamp and bundles of MSS. occupied another side of the room. The floor was carpeted while a rocker and chairs and some Biblical pictures on the walls furnished the remainder of the furniture.

"Just a moment while I go and call Mrs. Smith!" said the Minister. "She wishes very much to meet you, Mr. Miller!"

The minister left the room and Miller gazed around him. Examining the bookcases he found a general collection of literature as well as biblical books. Amongst the former were the complete works of Dickens, Scott and Thackeray; Gibbon's Decline and Fall of the Roman Empire, Macaulay's History of England, Guizot's History of France, Rambaud's History of Russia, History of United States, the Works of Washington Irving, of George Eliot, Hawthorne's Works, Dumas's Works; Cooper's Sea Tales, Cooper's Leather Stocking Tales, Encyclopædia Britannica, besides many individual books by noted authors—all of which proved the Rev. Mr. Smith to have a cultured mind.

Shortly the Rev. Mr. Smith and his wife entered the room. Mrs. Smith was a thin, fair woman of 26 or 28 years of age, with blue eyes, a small mouth and nose and a head of fluffy hair. She had a direct and unaffected manner and shook Miller warmly by the hand and welcomed him to their home.

"I have heard so much of what you have done for our Church here, Mr. Miller!" she exclaimed, "that I wished very much to make your acquaintance!"

"Oh! my puny efforts in the cause of religion have not amounted to much!" replied Miller.

The conversation then became general and after spending a pleasant evening at the clergyman's house John Miller returned to his own home in a pensive mood. His wife met him at the door.

"Well! How did you like the Smiths? Isn't he a delightful man and isn't she a dear?" asked his wife.

"Yes! They seem to be very nice people!" responded John. Her husband appeared to be very quiet the rest of the evening.

"John! What is the matter with you?" asked his wife on reaching their bedroom for the night.

"Nothing Mary! Nothing!" replied the husband.

"Why are you so quiet?" asked his wife, "What is wrong? One can't get a word out of you!"

"Nothing Mary! Nothing!" again replied her husband.

His wife made nothing more of it, thinking a good sleep would put her husband in a better humour the next morning.

But the next day and the day following that, Miller preserved his pensive deportment. He seemed to be intently considering a serious problem, and his wife thought it best not to interfere with him.

On the third evening after these occurrences Miller stated at the supper table to his wife he was going again to call on the Rev. Mr. Smith, and, stating he might be late in returning asked his wife not to sit up for him.

Reaching the minister's house, he was again ushered into the minister's den—his library—and found him busy as usual with some manuscript. Miller said at once on entering:

"Mr. Smith! You are a minister of God and I've come over here to ask you some questions which I would like settled for my own peace of mind!"

"Why! Yes! Certainly Mr. Miller. Any question of conscience I will most certainly endeavour to clear up —as far as I am able—for you!" answered the clergyman.

Miller stared at the floor for a few moments and then said:

"What sins will God not forgive?"

"God will forgive any sin for which there is true

repentance!" replied the Minister. " You know the Good Book says ' Repent and ye shall be forgiven!'"

" Yes! But are there not some sins which God will not forgive?" reiterated Miller, " for instance the sin against the Holy Ghost or the shedding of blood or murder?"

" There is no sin," again replied the minister, " for which there is no forgiveness providing the sinner truly repents of his sin!"

Miller appeared unconvinced and resting his elbows on his knees and holding his head between his hands stared moodily at the floor.

" Won't you tell me your troubles, Mr. Miller, and I will endeavour to the best of my poor ability to relieve them?" said the clergyman.

Miller shook his head, arose, took his hat and thanking the clergyman departed saying he would call again at another time.

The clergyman gazed after the departing figure of Miller, a doubtful expression on his face, because of the man's behaviour. Mrs. Smith coming into the room shortly after, her husband said " I am very much perturbed by John Miller's behaviour. He has been here for the past hour and will say very little and appears to have something on his mind—either that or the man is going insane!"

" Surely not!" cried his wife, " perhaps some business trouble is worrying him."

" I don't know, of course!" returned the husband, " but I don't think so! The man's mind is becoming unhinged!"

That evening John Miller again appeared at the clergyman's and was again admitted to the library. The clergyman now was partly convinced that Miller's mind was becoming unbalanced. He therefore adopted a soothing manner in his conversation with his parishioner. This Miller was quick to perceive and said :

" Do not fear, Mr. Smith—I am not insane nor going insane. I admit it is true, my behaviour here has been rather odd, but it is because I am worried about the salvation of my soul. I have called again to ask you if you are perfectly certain God will forgive any sin— any crime, however great—if the sin is thoroughly repented of ?"

" Yes !" replied the reassured clergyman. " We have the Sacred Book to substantiate that statement. Make a clean breast of your trouble, Mr. Miller, and I will endeavour to help you !"

" I have of course your word never to divulge what I am about to tell you !" said Miller, staring into the clergyman's face.

" Most certainly !" declared the clergyman. " At our ordination we were pledged to secrecy where secrecy was asked for !"

" Well ! I am troubled and I will tell you why. First, my name is not John Miller but John Haag. My mother's name was Miller and I adopted that name when I settled in this country. Ten years ago I murdered a man—Stephen Neubecker—over in Canada and was arrested, tried, convicted and hanged for the murder !" said Miller.

" Hanged for the murder and yet you are here ! Explain !" exclaimed the astonished clergyman.

Miller then related what had occurred, in the years that were gone; how that liquor and jealousy were the causes which led to the murder; how his father had mortgaged his farm to subvert the course of justice and hold up the arm of the law; how friendship and pity for his aged parents on the part of a Canadian doctor had made this feasible; how he was still amenable to

Canadian Law, if recognized and coming under its jurisdiction; how he had crossed to Michigan; adopted a new name in a new land and in new surroundings changed his mode of life and abandoned liquor; how after a few years of steady work at the trade of tailor, he had met and married his present dear wife and how finally doubts and fears as to his soul's welfare had begun to assail him since his acquaintance with the Rev. Mr. Smith.

The clergyman heard this tale with astonishment not unmixed with awe.

" How you must have suffered Mr. Miller, or rather Mr. Haag!" exclaimed the clergyman.

" No! No! Miller not Haag! The past is gone, and with it the old name. I am Miller here and always will be," he exclaimed.

" Yes!" Miller continued, " I suffered the tortures of the damned, mentally, during the three months I was awaiting execution in Walkerton gaol. And then what I suffered physically after the hanging because of the apparatus they had put on my neck and the effects of the rope. It was a month before I could move my head properly and for ten days thereafter I could not swallow without agony! Oh! What I suffered!" and Miller's face went pale at the thought.

" Well! Mr. Miller, it's all over now! I can assure you that if you heartily repent your sin God will forgive it. But you must repent in sackcloth and ashes your awful crime!" declared the clergyman.

" I do repent it!" cried Miller. " My God how I've cried and repented of it for years. I've cried out to God in my agony, for a sign that I'm forgiven, but no sign ever comes. Do you think he will forgive?" cried the agonized man.

" Most certainly He will forgive!" replied the

clergyman. "Set your mind at ease! There is balm for the sinner who repents!"

*   *   *   *   *

In a cosy farmhouse in Western Brant Township, Upper Canada, on an evening of that same Fall, a young couple, Mr. and Mrs. George Gordon (née Alice Beaumont) were sitting down to supper. Two curly-headed boys of 5 and 6 years of age occupied one side of the table, while a dark-eyed and dark-haired girl of 8 years—a replica on a small scale of Mrs. Gordon—occupied the other.

"I wonder if it's true, George, as people say, that Jack Haag escaped the gallows, and is living in Michigan?" said Mrs. Gordon.

"Nonsense!" answered George. "People are fond of talking! I saw him hanged! He's dead safe enough. His grave is out there just outside of Walkerton on the road to Glintz's Corners!"

Mrs. Gordon's eyes became misty.

"Poor Jack! What a bright and clever boy he was in the old school days, back in Woolwich and before he changed and took to drink and gambling"; and she heaved a sigh.

"Yes!" said George with a twinkle in his eye, "and they say it was you, Alice, who caused the change in him!" and he smiled at his wife. But a tear coursed down Mrs. Gordon's cheek and she said in a low voice—"Poor Jack. He cared for me anyhow! His one thought was of me!" and she gazed pensively at the table.

No woman can forget the man in whose breast she has instilled love and admiration.

THE END.

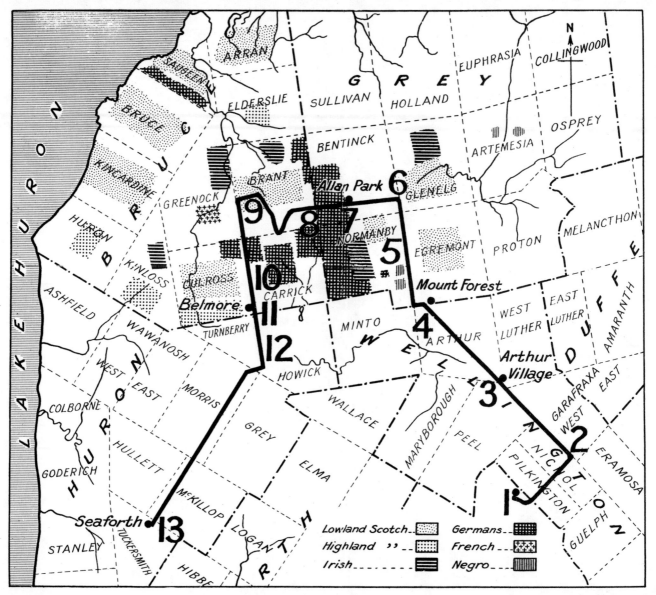